MAYDAY!
MAYDAY!

ALSO BY JULIE BRADLEY

Escape from the Ordinary
Crossing Pirate Waters

MAYDAY! MAYDAY!

MARINERS' GUIDE TO VHF RADIO

JULIE BRADLEY

Close Reach Publishing, LLC
First Printing, March 2022
©2022 Close Reach Publishing

Colophon is the trademark of Close Reach Publishing.

Cover design: Bloom Agency
Formatting: Cyndie Shaffstall

Library of Congress Control Number: 2022931836
Paperback ISBN: 978-1-7329184-5-0

Kindle ISBN: 978-1-7329184-6-7

The Library of Congress has cataloged as follows:
Bradley, Julie M.
MAYDAY! MAYDAY! Mariners' Guide to VHF Radio / Julie Bradley

Printed in the United States of America
DOC 10 9 8 7 6 5 4 3 2 1

CLOSE REACH
PUBLISHING

CONTENTS

To Glen. We've crossed oceans to end up back where we started. It feels like anything is possible when we're together.

Love and thanks to my nephew, Gabriel Maggiore, who inspired me to write this book and gave me the title.
May your life overflow with joy and adventure.

Author's Note

People I personally invite to read this book:
- Anyone who owns a boat.
- Anyone who crews on a boat.
- Anyone dreaming of the above.

Call It "Magic"

When a journalist asked Albert Einstein to explain radio communication, he reportedly replied: "You see, it is a kind of very, very long cat. You pull his tail in New York and his head is meowing in Los Angeles. Do you understand this? And radio operates exactly the same way: you send signals here; they receive them there. The only difference is that there is no cat."

Even Einstein struggled to explain the seeming wizardry of radio communication over invisible waves in the air. And those who did understand, would never have imagined that the 100-year-old technology would have developed in ways that make it more relevant and important now than ever. The lifesaving digital radio features in this book were developed to keep you, the mariner, safe. These new technologies make your VHF radio one of the most important pieces of safety equipment on your boat. Right up there with your GPS and life jacket!

INTRODUCTION

Another book on VHF communications!

I'm sure that's what many of you are thinking.

To an extent, you're right. There are lots of radio communication how-tos out there. And of course, for anyone who's listened to boaters on the VHF you have heard enough bad ones to think, "I can do THAT!" So, you may assume you don't need a book on how to communicate from a boat at all.

So why this one, and why is this book different?

To begin with, I've never seen a book on VHF communications that takes you out on the water with real-life scenarios. Other books pretend that all maritime emergencies are cookie-cutter situations with simple solutions. Read some of the complex distress calls within these chapters and you will understand why you need the solid skills to be gained here.

Secondly—and this is no slight to anyone—I think the person writing the book on marine radio skills should have a lot of experience communicating over the radio while crossing oceans, as well as travelling coastal, inland waters, and even on land—perhaps during military service. This is an area where I feel particularly qualified.

I first learned to use the VHF radio during my military career, then sailed around the world for eight years. A decade later, I traveled 6,000 miles of inland and coastal waters on America's Great Loop. And now, my husband and I spend winters on the Sea of Cortez in Mexico, where other boaters are your safety net.

Lastly, it would be a bonus if the person writing a VHF book gave you a sense and feel for the situations you might encounter on the water. Situations that feel so real the stories motivate you to become a pro, and then teach your crew. Then your crew can save your butt if you are the one with the medical emergency or are too busy trying to save your sinking boat to talk on the radio.

I've had a long track record of training people in both the military and on the water. During my years of training young soldiers, I learned that you better make the instruction as interesting as possible if you want to keep their attention. And I believe there are enough real-world scenarios in this book to keep yours.

So why another VHF book? Because the others I've seen don't give the simplified version in an easy-to-understand format. You don't need to know radio theory, wave propagation or the frequency spectrum. This guide skips anything you don't need to know. On top of that, other books often serve the writer of the VHF handbook more than the reader.

I don't want to travel around giving radio communication courses or seminars. I just want to pass along what I know to others who enjoy the water as much as I do. I've had a lot of amazing adventures (where extensive use of the radio was required) and want to keep on having them. Now I'd like to teach you, so you can pass this knowledge on to others.

CHAPTER 1

Why You Need This Guide

Picture yourself trolling for tuna on the aft deck of your boat. Your friend is hand-steering at the helm, and suddenly, the boat starts zigzagging erratically. Wondering if your friend is fooling around, you turn towards him, saying, *"What the ..."*. You stop midsentence, drop the fishing rod, and rush to your friend who is now on the deck clutching his chest, struggling to breathe.

You get the boat under control by throttling back to idle so you can attend to the medical emergency. With a pained expression, your friend whispers, "911, 911, call 911," before he passes out.

Land is beyond the horizon, and a glance at your phone shows no cell phone service. Anyway, you are out on the ocean, and no ambulance can get to you. Except the Coast Guard, right? You are on the edge of panic and decide to give CPR but know you should get help on the way.

You pick up your VHF radio to call the Coast Guard and suddenly freeze, asking yourself, *Is this a Mayday?*

The boat broker mentioned a button I was supposed to register with the Coast Guard. *Where's that button?*

You feel for a pulse. It's weak, and you squeeze your friend's hand, thinking, *please, don't die.*

You've found the distress button on your VHF radio. *Do I need to say anything after I push the button? Does the radio call the Coast Guard or other boats?*

Is this you? Are you confident about what to say on a VHF call and how to use the automatic distress function on your radio? Or its other digital capabilities? If not, keep reading.

Keeps It Simple

This handbook is unlike any other book on the topic of marine VHF radio operations. It covers everything you need to know without the burden of radio theory or frequency spectrum charts. In a couple of hours, you can learn about hailing friends, communicating with other boats, calling bridge and lock operators, as well as saving your own or someone else's life. This simplified format walks you step-by-step through the capabilities of your VHF radio as well as the lifesaving digital functions that automatically connect you to the Coast Guard during emergencies.

To give you a better feel for what can happen out on the water, I have included real-world distress scenarios of serious situations you might encounter. Learning from other boaters' emergencies will better equip you to handle your own. Whether you are sailing a small boat on lakes or sailing around the world, this book prepares you to conduct day-to-day operations; emergency distress calls, as well as how to communicate with boats outside the range of your VHF radio.

*****

Everyone on the Radio Started Out Like You

Though I used different types of radios to communicate during my Army career, my enthusiasm and respect for the VHF radio grew when I retired from the military, bought a boat, and sailed around the world.

During eight years of living aboard and crossing oceans, I used the radio daily. Military training, onboard experience and repetition gave me confidence in every aspect of radio communication. After completing an eight-year circum-navigation, I figured that radio skills were permanent, like riding a bike. But a decade later, when my husband and I boated the Great Loop of America, my skills were rusty. Moreover, old-fashioned radio technology had gone digital, making the marine VHF radio a powerhouse of lifesaving capabilities. Suddenly, I needed to update my radio skills for the 6,000-mile, yearlong journey ahead.

Traveling Busy Waters

If you are not familiar with America's Great Loop, it's a 6,000-mile voyage of Intracoastal and inland waterways circling the eastern part of the U.S. Along the route are some of the busiest waterways in the country, and you must have competent radio skills from day one.

Highly traveled waterways like the Loop take boaters along thousands of miles of inland navigation. You pilot your boat smack dab through the middle of sprawling cities such as Miami, Ft. Lauderdale, Savannah, Norfolk, New York, Chicago, St Louis—and many others.

Megayachts, pleasure boats, fishing boats, trawlers, pontoon boats all calling out on the radio to try to get ahead of each other. Passing a tug pushing 900 feet of barges tied four across down a narrow, winding river requires careful coordination over VHF radio as well as constant use of the digital features you learn about here.

In addition to everyday radio calls about passing other boats, bridge openings, and lock transits, I heard serious and life-threatening distress calls during our year on the Great Loop—three of them on one stormy day in Lake Erie. No matter what your ambitions, this book is well worth your time because VHF radio is the main, and sometimes ONLY form of communication on the water.

International Waters

The farther you sail from home waters the more important your VHF and overall radio skills become. In remote cruising grounds all boaters monitor Channel 16 and hail each other through their VHF radio. In some countries Coast Guard type services are rare or nonexistent and boaters rely on each other using their VHF radio when help is needed.

Preparing for the Unthinkable

The real-life distress stories in this handbook give examples of situations you may encounter. Thinking about them in advance will make you more effective and capable when the unthinkable happens. I share other stories to emphasize the importance of something that may not be obvious at first glance.

Written in simple terms anyone can understand, you do not need prior radio experience or a technical background. You *do* need to practice. The biggest challenge new learners face is getting out on the water enough to gain the practice and experience needed to hone their skills. Though real-world practice is the best, going over these scripts at home, away from your radio, is a close second.

Whether your desire is to sail around the world, travel the Great Loop, explore the islands, or enjoy waters closer to home, I hope one day you look back at *MAYDAY! MAYDAY! Mariners' Guide to VHF Radio* as a turning point in your overall marine skills.

CHAPTER 2

VHF Basics

Here we discuss the basics of VHF radio:

- Radio Types
- Hailing And Working Channels
- Congested Airwaves
- Typical VHF Radio Range
- Radio Checks
- Squelch

VHF Radio—Your New Best Friend

Alone on night watch, I was using both radar and night vision goggles to monitor heavy traffic in a major shipping channel. The radar alarm beeped, indicating our sailboat was on a collision course with another vessel. Peering at the radar I saw we would hit within 10 minutes at present speed. Surrounded by ships and jumpy from lack of sleep, my first impulse was to wake my husband, sleeping below. I hesitated. Glen had just gotten off watch and needed rest. As the person on duty, I was responsible for our lives and the operation of the boat. Establishing contact with that ship was my responsibility.

With a final glance at the radar, I cleared my throat, took a deep breath, and… glanced again at the radar. Maybe the ship has already turned course. No. It was even closer, and it was now or….

Keying the mic, I called the ship and spoke to my counterpart, the watch person on the bridge of the other vessel. The duty officer on the bridge told me he had not seen our sailboat on radar and thanked me for the call. In less than a minute, the other vessel and I had coordinated our courses and avoided collision.

The satisfaction and pride I felt were outsized considering the simple task at hand. Radio skills boosted my confidence and were vital in other tense situations during our eight-year circumnavigation.

I boldly say that this book will make you a better overall mariner. As your confidence with the radio builds, you will apply that competence to other nautical skills.

Like me, you will always remember that radio call when you made the transition from newbie to pro.

It's a Process

Getting comfortable with your radio will have its ups and downs. There will be times when you feel satisfied and proud of your ability—other times when you falter or become self-conscious. Go easy on yourself. Everyone you hear on the radio was once a novice and what you learn here will take the fear out of gaining the experience you need to improve.

*****

How Does it Work?

Every radio needs a specific "pipeline" to communicate over the airwaves. These "pipelines" are called channels and they each travel through the air at a different frequency. On the VHF radio you do not need to know about frequency because to simplify operation, a number has been assigned to each channel. The default channel on every VHF radio is Channel 16, used to hail other boats and call for help in distress.

Radio Types

There are three basic types of VHF radio units:
- Fixed mounts (also known as base units)
- Handhelds
- RAM mics (Remote Access Mics)

Let's take a quick look at each of these.

Fixed Mount or Base Unit VHF

A base unit VHF radio looks similar to this:

Typically, installers place base units in a protected, interior space—belowdecks at a navigation station or in the sheltered cockpit of a vessel. They are the most powerful VHF radios allowed by law at 25 watts of transmission power and require an external antenna.

On most boats, this means the antenna is higher up— usually at the top of a sailboat's mast or highest place possible on a powerboat. This height is essential to give your radio the farthest possible transmit and receive range. These radios may also have built-in advanced features such as Automatic Identification System (AIS), Digital Selective Calling (DSC) , and Global Positioning System (GPS), which are new lifesaving digital capabilities we will cover in depth further ahead.

VHF antennas are mounted as high as possible.

Handheld VHF Radio

Handheld VHF Radio

A handheld VHF radio looks like a walkie-talkie but is, in fact, a fully functioning portable VHF radio. Handhelds are often waterproof and sometimes made to float, clip to a belt, or hang from a lanyard for easy access. They have a built-in antenna and are less powerful than base units. Base units have 25 watts of power, whereas handheld versions usually have only 5 watts. Calls from a handheld VHF won't reach as far as those from a base unit. Handhelds often lack the more advanced features found on a fixed-mount radio, such as AIS, DSC, and GPS. Handheld VHF radios are often used from a boat's cockpit to call bridges and other nearby boats and are great to take along in a dinghy.

Remote Access Microphone (RAM)

Remote Access Microphone (RAM)

Weather-resistant RAM mics have the strength, range, and capabilities of the base unit with the convenience and functions of a handheld. That's because they are a remote microphone connected by cable to the fixed-mount base unit. The remote mic offers the same functionality and power as the base station at a different location on the boat, usually the helm. This location protects the base unit from turbulent weather while giving the radio operator full radio function at the wheel. Remote mics provide a helm station with greater power, range, and talk time than a handheld VHF.

Remote mics are available on newer designs of base units. The base unit is installed in a protected and convenient location belowdecks, while the RAM mic is wired into the cockpit or helm for use while underway.

Remote microphones for fixed VHF radios are great tools for coastal and blue water sailors and essential for short-handed crews. When leaving the helm or tiller isn't an option, the watch person can safely communicate even in choppy weather.

Remote mics provide a helm station with greater power, range, and talk-time than a handheld VHF; however, they do not offer the redundancy of a second fixed VHF or limited-range handheld. They are a cost-efficient and a weather-safe way to get full base-unit function and transmission range into the cockpit without relocating your fixed-mount radio.

A remote-access microphone at the helm with a base unit protected from the weather brings the base unit's full functions to the helm without risking sensitive electronics.

Hailing and Working Channels

When you wish to speak with someone on another vessel, you hail them. It isn't a conversation yet because you don't know if they are available. You hail other vessels or the Coast Guard, to attempt to start a conversation.

Wait! I Thought Channel 16 is Reserved for Distress Calls?

Channel 16 is the default channel programmed into your VHF radio. Channel 16 *is* primarily for distress calls. For decades it has also been used to hail other boats. The Coast Guard is trying to retrain us, and we will cover that further on. Since most boats still hail another boat on Channel 16, here is the correct protocol to limit crowded airwaves.

After hailing another boat on Channel 16, it is important that you both switch from channel 16 to a **working channel**. A working channel is where you are permitted to talk as long as there is no other radio traffic on that specific channel at the time. Remember, **channel 16 is reserved for hailing and communicating distress calls. You must keep channel 16 clear for these purposes.**

Congested Airwaves

Talking on the VHF is not like talking on your cell phone, and it is not for conversations or catching up on what's been happening since you last saw a friend. That makes more sense when you understand that when you talk on the radio you are broadcasting over a public airwave. Your radio conversation blocks the airwaves on that channel for about a 20-mile radius when your radio is on high power (we will talk more about low and high power in the next section). Even finding a clear working channel can be frustrating in populated areas. However, there are things we can all do to help ease the congestion.

Channel 16 must be kept clear for emergency calls and hailing. Keep your call brief, plan which working channel you will use before hailing, verify the receiving party heard the channel you are switching to, and then switch immediately to the working channel.

Even after switching to a working channel, remember that the VHF radio is for boat operations. You can use it to make plans to meet someone ashore, pass along weather information, or tell another boat where you are headed—but it isn't the place to chat.

Stay aware of the conversations you have, keep them brief, move them to an allowable working channel, and limit them to boating-related topics. Reducing congestion on the airwaves makes boating safer for everyone on the water.

Typical VHF Radio Range

VHF signals only operate in a straight line, so are 'line of sight'. How far the VHF signal can travel depends on the heights of the sending and receiving antennas. Note: VHF radios can only receive VHF transmissions

Two factors determine how far you can transmit and receive radio traffic: antenna height and transmission power. VHF radio waves work by line of sight, which means your radio signals are streaming out in a straight line. On the open water, the curvature of the earth or the horizon becomes the limiting factor to your line of sight. Note that the higher your VHF antenna is mounted on your boat, the greater the transmitting distance and reception.

Marine VHF radios are legally limited to 25 watts of transmission power. They must have a high and low power option that allows the user to select low (1 watt) transmission power (see High Power vs. Low Power later in this handbook) and high (25 watt) transmission power.

Transmissions made at a lower power have less strength and travel less far. Even though it sounds strange, sometimes a weaker signal is better, and I'll talk about why that may be so in a later section, building on what you learn here.

Handheld radios always have lower overall power than fixed mount radios (typically around 5 watts maximum). The antenna is attached to the radio itself, and typically used while lower on a boat than a permanently fixed base antenna. This low placement decreases the transmission range.

Remember, your radio is only half of the connection. The same factors that limit your radio, such as antenna height and transmitting power, also affect the other person's radio in the same way. Trial and error will help you determine how far your transmissions will travel and what traffic you can hear on any given day. Typical base unit and remote access microphone boat-to-boat traffic may go about 12 miles on high power (mast-top to masttop without obstruction as much as 20 miles or more). In comparison, handhelds may be limited to about a mile.

Radio Checks

Imagine you call a vessel ahead to confirm a port-to-starboard pass and they never answer. Later that same day, you call for a bridge opening and get no reply. *"Is my radio even working?"* you wonder. Then you remember hearing other boaters calling "Radio check! Radio check!" on channel 16, and you remember the waves of responses saying, "Loud and clear!"

"Maybe I should do that," you think.

You SHOULD NOT. Do NOT request radio checks on channel 16.

Radio checks clog the airwaves. For miles and miles around your boat channel 16 will be blocked as boaters in the area ask if they can be heard and other boats respond. This chatter might prevent someone from being heard when they are in distress.

There is, however, an acceptable way to ease your mind about your radio signal strength.

Instead, say, **"Radio check. Radio check,"** on **channel 09** and await a reply. You can use this channel because it is not a distress channel, and the Coast Guard has designated it as an alternate hailing channel. You won't risk blocking someone's emergency call hailing on Channel 09. Help keep channel 16 clear for important traffic by *making your radio checks responsibly on channel 09.*

Squelch and How it Works

Another radio feature that impacts what calls you may or may not be able to hear is squelch. Squelch is a filtering mechanism. It suppresses incoming trans- missions that fall below a certain signal strength, and it stops these weaker signals before they are sent to your radio's speaker. This allows you to keep static and weak, unintelligible radio calls silenced.

All VHF radios come with this adjustable function. Understanding squelch is essential. Even minor adjustments to the squelch setting can block or allow a tremendous amount of static to make it through to your radio speaker. It is commonplace to adjust squelch to the lowest setting, which makes your radio mostly static- free. If you start hearing a lot of static, you can adjust the squelch higher. You want the squelch as low as possible, while still eliminating static, to filter out most of the weak, longrange calls outside your area.

Suppose you attempt to have a conversation with a vessel far away or one transmitting to you on lower power. In that case, you may need to adjust the squelch down temporarily to receive the distant ship's transmission. It may be scratchy because squelch filters out static, but it may also enable you to communicate. You can adjust it slightly higher after your call, but remember, a lot of radio traffic may not make it through if you turn up the squelch too high. The more you speak on the radio, the more comfortable you will be adjusting the squelch.

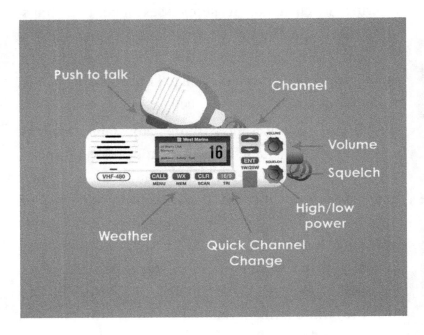

VHF radio features differ by manufacturer, but the illustration above is a typical layout. If you bought a boat with a VHF radio and cannot find the manual, you can find it online and print it to keep as a handy reference. In an emergency, you will be glad you took the time to get to know your specific radio.

Later in this guide, I will discuss functions seen in the above illustration.

*****

As promised, you are learning all you need to know about VHF radio operations in this simplified handbook. So far, I have introduced you to the three types of VHF radios, hailing and working channels, typical range, factors that affect range, making a radio check, and squelch. Now let's move on and learn how to make radio calls. Remember that Channel 16 is used for both distress and hailing. Once the boat you hail responds, you MUST both switch to a working channel to converse.

*****

FUN FACT: *The first incident of telephone hold music was a mistake caused by a loose wire touching a metal girder at a factory. It turned the entire building into a mega radio antenna that would play the music from a next-door radio station when people were on hold.*

CHAPTER 3

Radio Call Fundamentals

Making great radio calls doesn't just *happen*, nor is it a factor of years spent on the water. Becoming a pro is about knowing and reinforcing correct procedures. Many mariners spend years using bad radio protocol. And I'm sorry, but when you hear someone on the radio with sloppy or poor protocol, there is a tendency to think that lack of mastery extends to their other marine skills. Don't be that person!

This chapter gives you the tools you need to make those calls correctly and ways to become a pro. For starters, pay attention to others talking on the radio. With the skills learned here, you'll start noticing who knows what they are doing and those who do not. Besides the pride of being a capable mariner, knowing that everyone within the range of your radio is listening is great motivation.

The important concepts of this chapter:

- Wind
- How to Speak
- Push to Talk (PTT)
- Open Mics
- High Power vs. Low Power
- Public Airwaves

Wind

We've all seen weather reporters trying to talk in hurricane force winds. Well, even moderate wind can interfere with the sensitive microphone of your VHF radio.

Transmit from a protected space to avoid wind interference.

It is common to hear radio traffic between one party who is clear and easy to understand and a second party who has no idea that standing in the wind in the cockpit of their boat makes them impossible to understand. The effect of wind hitting your radio mic makes for noisy transmission. Wind transmits in the background like a freight-train regardless of your signal strength.

If you have no option to get out of the weather, turn your back to the wind. But it's better if you can get under the dodger or shelter in some other protected space. In extreme conditions make your calls from belowdecks, fully out of the wind. Mentally evaluate your wind situation before you make a call.

How to Speak

To be understood you must speak clearly and directly into the mic, while trying to retain natural speech patterns. Attempts to over-enunciate words do not lead to better understanding. However, slowing down your speech DOES help the listener.

New radio users tend to want to get the experience over with quickly. Instead, rushing does the opposite. Think about what you are going to say ahead of time and take it slowly. When you are just starting out it is better to say it slowly and clearly *once* than repeat it because the listener could not catch what you said.

Feeling nervous can make some of us talk more than we should. Avoid the tendency to be overly conversational, especially on channel 16. Hailing vessels or bridges is not the time for excess conversation or making new friends. It's all about getting the message across correctly the first time and freeing up the channel for use by others. When just starting out it is best to rehearse in your mind and then say out loud what you are going to say. Be clear and be direct, expressing yourself in as few words as possible while sounding natural. Rehearse it first and you will do great.

Push to Talk and Release to Listen

All VHF radios are **Push to Talk**. This means that your radio cannot transmit and receive at the same time. When you key the mic button—when you **Push** it **To Talk**—you are momentarily switching the radio from *receive* mode to *transmit* mode. When you are pushing the transmit button, **you cannot hear anything. To listen to radio traffic, you must release the button, otherwise you continue to transmit**.

Be sure to fully press the mic key in before you start to speak and fully release it once you are done so that you can hear again. Unlike a cellphone, only one of you can be heard at a time. Pace your conversations with the normal give and take of two people talking and remember to **push to talk** and **release to listen**.

Open Mics

During your boating you will inevitably hear an endless transmission from someone whose radio mic has been keyed (pressed) accidentally. They may be leaning against the mic button, or something is pressed against their radio. All the background clamor from their boat—wind noise, conversations, and music—fills the airwaves as they unwittingly transmit a conversation with their buddy. Called a *hot* mic, those situations are a danger as well as a nuisance.

Annoying to all and even worse, they are blocking the airwaves from important traffic.

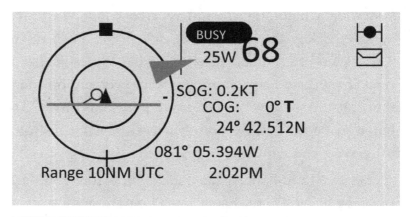

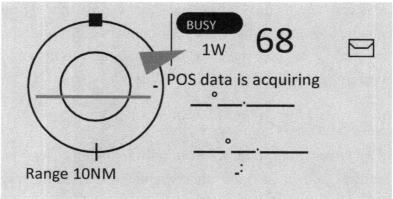

Radios display settings to indicate high power or low power and most have an easy-to-find button to switch the radio from one to the other.

When that happens you will hear folks try to *help* by rushing to broadcast an announcement that "someone has a hot mic!" But guess what? As you learned in the Push to Talk section above, the person with the hot mic can't hear you until that microphone transmit button is released.

Be aware of your radio's microphone and ensure it can't accidentally transmit.

High Power vs. Low Power

By law, all VHF radios, whether fixed-mount or handheld, come with a high- and low-power feature. High power on a fixed-mount radio is typically the legal maximum of 25 watts, and on a handheld, high power is usually 5 or perhaps 6 watts—much lower than that of the fixed radio. All radios must **have a low power option, which on your handheld radio transmission means just 1 watt of power.**

Lower power means a weaker signal, so if maximum distance is your goal, you will want the radio in high power mode, and you will want to use the more-powerful fixedmount radio instead of the handheld radio. But suppose you are calling a boat anchored next to you in the harbor?

Instead of alerting everyone within a 20-mile radius of the purpose of your call—perhaps that your dinghy has come free and is floating away—switch that radio to low power or grab a handheld. Any boat or bridge within a half-mile should still pick up your signal just fine, and you will help the boating community by not unnecessarily sharing your conversation over the airwaves for miles and miles.

Default power on *channel 16* will *always* be 25 watts—**high power.** When you need to make an emergency announcement you will appreciate every watt of it.

But when the opportunity arises, use less power. Distant boaters will thank you.

Develop a Code

In an age of cellular communication, it is easy to forget that VHF conversations go out over public airwaves, for all to hear. Discussing information about where you are anchored, what time you will dinghy ashore or meet up for dinner at a restaurant ashore is information that **could be overheard by those with ulterior motives.**

When buddy boating it is common to create nicknames for friends and friends' boats to keep from sharing more than necessary. It's a good idea to move conversations about specific plans to a smartphone text message if you have cell service. This caution is not intended to make you paranoid, but good safety habits keep boating enjoyable.

*****

Keyed Mic Example

While sailing around the world we spent four years in the South Pacific, exploring as many islands as possible. However, our boat insurance required us to leave the six-month-long hurricane season in the tropical islands. Our solution was to sail to New Zealand for six months, out of tropical cyclone territory.

When Team New Zealand hosted the iconic America's Cup sailing competition, we were there in Auckland, living on our boat. Wanting to be as close to the sailing action as possible, we volunteered to help with the race series. Kiwis love sailors, and gave us weighty, full-time jobs as course marshals. It was long, hard work under the best conditions, but extra difficult when the wind piped up. The finely engineered racing boats could have structural failure in winds over 20 knots, so races were canceled when high winds were forecast. However, low-level workers like us were frustrated to have to stay out on the water tacking around in rough conditions—sometimes for hours—until the race committee made an official decision to cancel.

A month into the race series, the winds were blowing 30, and gusting higher. The race teams knew the race would be cancelled and stayed at the docks, but the support boats had to report for duty in the heavy wind and high waves. The boat that laid out the course markers was instructed to go ahead and lay the racing buoys, even though by the time they were down they would have to be picked up.

No one had to guess the annoyance and anger of the course marker boat; they put the VHF mic in the cup holder instead of back on the radio set. The side of the cup holder pressed against the mic and any boat within VHF range heard their conversation and complaints about certain people in charge. Boats all over Auckland increased the volume on their radios to better hear them, until finally, the race committee reached them on a cell phone and told them to unkey their mic. That day's race was called off moments afterward and we all returned to base.

Moral to the story: Don't be that person who ties up the distress channel because of a keyed mic!

CHAPTER 4

Making Radio Calls

There's no rule that says you can only enjoy something if you are already good at doing it. Case in point are all those people who can't carry a tune that go to karaoke clubs, get on stage, and belt out a song.

Just like every other aspect of boating and sailing, the key to getting good is **practice**. To do that you must be willing to be less than perfect while practicing. Having the courage to cringe when you make mistakes on the airwaves is the only way you will get enough experience for it to come naturally. Do not fear the cringe. Cringing is a sure sign that you are getting better.

Think of mastering radio communications not as one skill, but as part of a set of processes that are linked together to become a better mariner. Working to improve one area lifts the whole. Each time you mindfully listen to others communicating on the radio and think about what you are going to say before keying the mic, you are becoming a better mariner.

Adopt that attitude and one day, out of nowhere, someone will ask you how you got so good using the radio.

Now that we've covered types of equipment and best practices, let's talk about how to make routine radio calls. In this section we'll cover step-by-step details for making the three most common types of calls so you can start practicing:

- Hailing a Familiar Boat
- Hailing a Vessel You Do Not Know
- Hailing Locks and Bridges

One of 57 locks and 17 lift bridges in the New York State Canal System where you need to know what you are doing on the VHF radio.

Let's start with the simplest and most-common call: to another, known boat.

Great Loop boats often travel in posse, like the cowboys in the Old West! Except they call it buddy boating and their horsepower runs on fuel instead of hay.

Hailing a Familiar Boat

Let's say I am anchored on a boat named *Star Dust* and spot a friend sailing into the anchorage aboard a boat named *Double Trouble*. I decide to radio them and let them know there is a good spot near me where they can safely anchor. What do I do?

We have a lot to think about before hailing *Double Trouble*. Are the airwaves busy? How far away is the boat I am hailing? If my friend is a mile or so away, and my call is not a priority, I may choose to hail them from my strong fixed-mount radio. Should I switch the power to low when I go to my working channel to avoid interfering with radio traffic farther away? Let's walk through the example and I will answer these questions and more.

Decide Which Channel to Use for Hailing

My first contact will be on channel 16, the hailing and distress channel. The overwhelming majority of first contact boat-to-boat hailing happens on Channel 16, and the few exceptions to this are addressed later in the channel overview section.

Pre-select a Working Channel

If *Double Trouble* answers my call, I must have a working channel already chosen because I cannot have a conversation on channel 16. With experience, you will develop a favorite channel you know is not full of local radio traffic. Even then, you should give it a quick listen to ensure there isn't a conversation already underway. Two pairs of boats in VHF range (within 10 – 15 miles of each other) cannot share the same working channel.

For this example, I choose channel 69 as my working channel (see listed options later in the channel overview section), flip to it to ensure there is no traffic, and hearing none, determine it is a good choice for the conversation.

Start Your Call

The name of my vessel is *Star Dust*, and I am calling *Double Trouble*. With my radio on channel 16, I firmly key the mic and say the target vessel's name two to three times, followed by a very short pause and then my vessel's name. This call would sound like this:

"Double Trouble, Double Trouble. Star Dust"

Now I wait for a response. The boat you are calling might be dropping anchor and it could take a few minutes to get to the radio. If I do not get a response after waiting a couple minutes, I will try **one more time** in the same manner.

"Double Trouble, Double Trouble. Star Dust"

If I still get no answer, I wait a while and try later. I do not clutter the airwaves with constant calls to a boat that is not replying. Most things on the water can wait. After all, that is why we are attracted to the laidback life of the water.

If *Double Trouble* replies, their response might be something like this:

"This is Double Trouble." or "Go ahead, Star Dust."

Now I reply and instruct *Double Trouble* to switch to the working channel I cleared before making this call. In this case channel 69 was free of other traffic. It is common practice to say the channel's two numbers individually for clarity, "six-nine". Because there are a lot of boats out there, I say my friend's boat's name again, so everyone knows who I am addressing:

"Double Trouble, switch to six-nine."

The vessel *receiving* my request to move to a working channel should confirm the channel before switching so we know both parties correctly heard the request. *Double Trouble* might reply something like this:

"Copy. Six-nine." or "Switching six-nine."

We both switch our radios to channel 69 to hold our conversation.

You've made your first radio call!

Wait!

How Many Times Should You Say the Other Boat's Name?

It is technically correct to say the hailing and target vessel's names three times, and although repeating three times is common practice in Canadian waters, you rarely hear it three times in American or Bahamian cruising grounds—other than by the US Coast Guard.

The target vessel's name is commonly repeated only twice in good radio conditions. Vessels may repeat this three times if contact is not immediate, if the target vessel is somewhat distant from the hailing ship, or if the airways are experiencing much radio traffic or static.

Hailing a boat to coordinate passing.

Hailing a Boat or Ship You Do Not Know

While motoring north off the ICW, a motor yacht came up fast behind us, moving a fair bit faster than our boat. Thinking that the boat's captain might be hesitant to pass in a narrow part of the river—though there was enough room—I decided to call out to him on the VHF.

Things get a little more complicated when you don't know the name of a vessel you are calling, but with just a few pointers you will feel comfortable.

First, call out to the other boat just as you would if you knew its name. To do this you will refer to it as whatever kind of vessel it is, "motor vessel," "tug and barge," or "sailing vessel," in lieu of its name, along with its direction of travel, hull color, and geographical location. Since there are so many variables it helps to think through what you plan to say before keying the mic.

Then identify yourself as the hailing vessel, remembering that they also do not know you or your boat. To do this you will use a description of your boat as well as its location relative to the vessel you are hailing. The image below shows the language to use to describe your vessel's relationship to another boat.

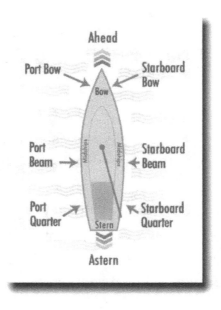

My VHF call sounded like this:

"Northbound motor yacht approaching Bucksport—this is the motor vessel Star Dust off your bow."

And the motor yacht responded:

"This is Legacy here, go ahead."

NOTE: Our vessels were quite close together, and this was extremely late in the season in a desolate stretch of the waterway. The VHF radio had been virtually silent all day. Because of this, I did not repeat my description of the target vessel twice, although I usually would (and technically should). Had he not quickly responded I would have repeated my hailing call of "Northbound motor yacht approaching Bucksport" at least twice for clarity. Every situation is different, but with the information here and a bit of practice you will develop a feel for just how strictly to follow standard protocol.

After switching to a working channel, I proceeded to let him know that I was happy to let him pass me on my port side, which he accepted.

If you are in busy waters and receive a response from your target vessel, *take a moment to acquire more detail* that the proper vessel has replied after you switch to your chosen working channel. You will hear complete conversations with **incorrect vessels that responded to what sounded like very clear calls. VHF radios** transmit as far as **25 miles and there are a lot of boats out there. Double-check after you switch!**

Hailing Locks and Bridges

If you are planning a trip down the ICW or perhaps traveling the Great Loop, hailing drawbridges and locks will become a common part of your daily routine. Here is how to safely and effectively call bridges and locks.

NOTE: In this section, the term drawbridge includes lift bridges, swing bridges, bascule bridges, pontoon bridges, railroad bridges, and any other bridge that you would hit if a bridge operator didn't open it for you ahead of time. And while going through a lock may be quite different than going through a drawbridge,

hailing one or the other is the same. This section works for locks as well.

Understand that there is no perfect formula for calling drawbridges. Here are some pointers, however, to help you get through with optimal success and minimal stress.

Know the Bridge's VHF Operating Channel

Some states use 09, some use 13. Some bridges monitor 16 and some do not. Have your information source prepared before you set out so that you can transit these bridges or locks without undue difficulty. Sources include electronic charts, *Active Captain*, and cruising guides such as *The Waterway Guide*.

Listen Ahead

Listening in on the bridge hailing channel (most commonly 09 or 13) before you reach the bridge will offer much information as to how to best proceed. Is the bridge tender admonishing other vessels for calling for an opening too late (too close to the bridge)? Or perhaps too early (too far away from the bridge)? Bridges are staffed by human beings with human strengths and weaknesses. They do not want to anger motorists by making them wait longer than necessary. At all times be courteous and patient. The bridge tender controls everything.

Know the Bridge's Name

Take a few moments to look at your charts and determine the name of the bridge. You could wait a long time if you call bridges by the wrong name or expect the bridge to open without communicating to the bridge tender. On days when you may pass through multiple bridges, it can help to make a list of all of the day's expected bridges and their respective schedules and VHF channels prior to setting off. This makes finding the next bridge's information quick and painless while underway.

Know the Bridge's Schedule

Just like you looked up the name, know the bridge's schedule long before you reach it. Is it scheduled? Or on demand? Are there rush hour, construction, weekend, or holiday restrictions? This information is found along with the proper VHF channel for that bridge from your chosen chart, guide, or other source.

On-Demand Actually Means On-Request

The bridge tender has the OPEN button and all the authority. You need them. Stay humble in your calls, and without any extra conversation politely **request an opening.**

Step-by-Step Drawbridge Call

Tilghman Island Drawbridge on the Chesapeake Bay

Follow these steps to make a good bridge call:

Time your call so you are close to the bridge but not too close. It is really a judgment decision. If the cars on the bridge still look like specks you're too far! If you already had to go to neutral or even started circling to avoid hitting the bridge fenders, you're too close. Ideally, you will be a comfortable 5 or so minutes away from the bridge, with room to slow down or speed up as needed.

Knowing the bridge's name, schedule, and VHF operating channel, proceed to hail the bridge **on its specified VHF channel (not channel 16)** by calling its name two times, followed by a very short pause and then the name of your vessel. Nothing more, yet.

Your initial call to the bridge is to make contact, not to make your opening request.

Here is a call to the very real Old Roosevelt Bridge in Stuart, Florida.

The first thing to do is to hail the bridge (in Florida, bridges are hailed on channel 09):

"Old Roosevelt Bridge, Old Roosevelt Bridge—Star Dust."

After the bridge tender replies, respond back with a very basic description of your vessel type (sailing, motor, trawler etc.), your general direction of travel, and the details of your request (unless you are asked a specific question). Typically, vessels traveling on the ICW tend to refer to **southbound or northbound in the greater perspective of ICW travel regardless of the actual compass heading as they approach the bridge.**

The bridge might simply respond with:

"This is Old Roosevelt. *"*

To which we would reply something along the lines of:

"Old Roosevelt we are a northbound sailing vessel and would like to request your 11 am opening."

At this point the bridge would typically reply letting us know when they will be opening and perhaps where they expect our vessel to be at opening time. After acknowledging this, we would stand by on the bridge hailing channel.

Old Roosevelt bridge tender:

"Copy that, captain. If you are close enough when I start the 11:00 opening, we'll let you through."

Us:

"Copy that, Old Roosevelt. Star Dust standing by, zero-nine."

The bridge hailing channel is where the bridge might announce the beginning (or delay) of the opening and where other vessels passing through on the same opening might contact you to clarify navigation questions if there are lots of boats circling until the opening time. Some bridges will ask you to repeat your vessel's name or perhaps to spell it, or they may ask you for your hailing port. After safely transiting the open bridge, it is common courtesy to briefly call the bridge to announce that you are clear of the bridge's spans and to thank the tender for the opening. Avoid the temptation to go on at length here. A simple and polite announcement is all that is needed:

"Old Roosevelt—Star Dust is clear. Thank you for the opening."

Remember: bridges are staffed by human beings. They may be having a good day, or…they may not. Following these tips will help to ensure that your boat's passage through a bridge will be a positive part of their day and yours.

A Note About Approaching Drawbridges

Generally, vessels traveling **with the current have priority over those traveling against** it. This is not worth arguing about with unknowledgeable boaters unless the currents or winds are strong enough to make navigation difficult or hazardous. You can reach out to other boats at a bridge opening to clarify traffic priorities before the bridge opens by hailing them on the bridge channel.

You may not hear many boaters do this, but safety and goodwill are the rewards of good communication. An example of a bridge traffic call might sound like:

"Southbound motor vessel at Old Roosevelt Bridge — this is the northbound sailing vessel, Harmony."

"This is September Song. Go ahead."

"Captain, we're coming through from the north side and have a stiff current behind us. I would appreciate it if you'd let us pass through first."

If you cannot see the other boat to know what type of vessel it is, you can use the generic term "traffic" or "vessel," such as "southbound traffic at Old Roosevelt Bridge."

Remember that not all boats are easily maneuverable, especially sailboats. Some vessels may wait with bow pointed at the bridge, others may turn backwards to point into the current or wind, and some may just spin in slow circles. Every boat and every boater handles their boat differently.

It is common courtesy to stay in your general place in line before a bridge unless otherwise communicated on the radio. That old, slow sailboat at the front of the line may have plenty of tempting and empty water next to it—and they may be just about to turn into it to avoid their forestay hitting the bridge. Stay in your general spot unless agreed upon in advance.

*****

Transiting a lock in the Erie Canal on America's Great Loop, Glen said into the radio handset, while nudging the engines to keep us in place. Five other boats were doing the same, trying to avoid collision in the narrow waiting area below the lock.

"Lock 2, Lock 2, this is motor vessel Star Dust, requesting westbound passage."

Scanning the deck, I felt as ready as possible; there would be no time to correct anything once in the lock. White fenders hung at various lengths, and from the side resembled the pipes of an organ. Planning to transit on the port side of the lock, I stood at the center cleat to quickly shift fenders if we were told to move to the starboard side of the chamber. It would be a scramble, but…I smiled nervously at Glen up on the flybridge helm and took a deep breath. This was a big day for me and *Star Dust*.

Star Dust is the fifth boat back

So far, we had transited 8 locks on *Star Dust*, and understood there would be a total of 149 locks on the Great Loop. To read that number before we started the Loop on *Star Dust* was one thing. To really understand what it means through experience is widely different. On the plus side, the coming weeks would lop off a large percentage of that total number; 36 locks lay between *Star Dust* and the Great Lakes. To think about that number was overwhelming so I focused on getting through the lock ahead. *Star Dust* confided that she, too, had a bit of performance anxiety at this first and most famous section of the Erie Canal; the Waterford Flight.

A Long Way Up

Waterford Flight is a combined lift. Five separate locks within 1.5 miles of each other raise boats just over 169 feet. A dizzying height by any measure. Anxiety shifted to reality as the radio crackled, "*Star Dust, Star Dust, Lock 2*. An eastbound vessel is exiting the gate now. When you see the green light signal, follow the other boats and tie up any side."

'Roger, *Lock 2*," Glen responded, then slowly powered Star Dust toward what is basically a water elevator. Boats enter the lock at one floor and get out at another a few floors up or down depending on which direction they are traveling. Manhole sized openings beneath the water surface let water in or out, letting gravity do all the work. To get an idea of the forces at play, it takes around 110,000 gallons to raise or lower water in the chamber one foot. So, the 169 feet lift within the first five locks would be…a LOT of water.

"Get ready," said Glen, giving me a thumbs up. In turn I patted *Star Dust*, telling her, "You got this."

A sailboat with its mast unstepped and tied on deck exited past us from the lock. When the light turned green, we pulled into the narrow chute with five larger boats crowding the small space. Before we were even settled, two 60 ft. tall gates shut behind us with a metallic clang. Making room along the chamber wall, Glen jockeyed the throttles of the twin engines, inching us down the lock. There was a fine line between making room for the other, bigger boats and keeping clear of gates holding back massive amounts of water.

Now to Grab a Line

Once in the lock each boat must secure themselves to the lock wall. A few pipes or taut steel cables are sometimes set into recesses in the walls. Most have only fixed ropes, weighted at the end, intended to hold you in position as the lock lifts or lowers. As I quickly learned, a single, slimy rope tied some 60' above your head does not do much to keep a boat from moving away from the wall or pivoting toward other boats as eddies swirl in the filling lock.

Hang on Star Dust

It seemed to take forever for gravity to fill the chamber with water from the high side. My arms throbbed trying to manhandle the green, algae covered ropes, too swollen and thick to safely cleat.

I would like to say that having transited the mighty Panama and Suez Canals on our circumnavigation, that Glen and I were models of excellence during all five locks of the Waterford Flight. But that would be incorrect. Tension was high and it took the full force of our energy to keep from crashing us into other boats. There was plenty of shouting on all the boats as gusting wind upped the challenge.

My shoulders finally relaxed as *Star Dust* rose above the bollards and the water calmed. Gravity and the lock had done its job. As Glen motored *Star Dust* toward the next lock, I sat on deck, leaned back, and pondered the many locks ahead on the Erie Canal—and 149 total on the Great Loop.

What cheered me from that thought was history. Exiting the first lock I looked to the side and saw the 40-footwide chamber of the narrow, original lock built in 1825.

If we had a mule pulling us on that towpath this would be a lot easier," I told Glen.

"*Star Dust* can't carry enough hay for the trip," he answered.

Me when we were transistioning a lock on the Great Loop.

A Quick Review

We've covered radio basics such as hailing and working channels. You know your radio's range on high and low power and when you might want to use one or the other. You learned tips and tricks to make sure you can be understood from the cockpit. And we went step-by-step through calls to boats we know, boats we don't know, and to drawbridges. You've learned a lot already!

Now that you have a solid foundation, let's dig a little deeper into other aspects of radio life. In the following sections we are going to talk about the channels on your radio and which ones are okay for you to use. We will look at radio lingo to use and radio lingo to avoid. And we will examine features that your radio

may have, and for safety *should have*, like DSC and AIS.

*****

Here's a good story told to me by a Canadian on the Great Loop that shows how important it is to verify who you are communicating with, especially when using radar to navigate. It's fictional but carries the point!

Americans:

"Please divert your course 15 degrees to the North to avoid a collision."

Canadians:

"Recommend you divert YOUR course 15 degrees to the south to avoid a collision."

Americans:

"This is the Captain of a US Navy ship. I say again, divert YOUR course."

Canadians:

"No. I say again you divert YOUR course."

Americans:

"THIS IS THE AIRCRAFT CARRIER USS LINCOLN, OF THE UNITED STATES' ATLANTIC FLEET. WE ARE ACCOMPANIED BY THREE DES-TROYERS, THREE CRUISERS, AND NUMEROUS SUPPORT VESSELS. I DEMAND THAT YOU

CHANGE COURSE. ALL MEASURES WILL BE UNDERTAKEN TO ENSURE THE SAFETY OF THIS SHIP."

Canadians:

"This is a lighthouse. Your call."

CHAPTER 5

Channel Guide to VHF Radio

VHF Channel Rules—What Channel to Use in Different Situations

What VHF Channel Should I Use?

By now we all know the importance of keeping Channel 16 clear for distress and hailing calls, but what about the other channels? Can you use the others anytime you want? No.

Every VHF marine radio channel has a use designation. By paying attention to which channels you're supposed to be talking on, you minimize the chance of interfering with someone else's conversation. For safety purposes, boats should **monitor channel 16 at all times**, and it is the default channel built into VHF radios.

Channel 16 is also a hailing frequency, but the airwaves are so crowded with boaters that in high traffic areas, the USCG urges sailors and boaters to hail other boats on channel 9 to keep 16 open to distress calls. You will hear the Coast Guard announce that request periodically in busy waters. The Coast Guard values lives over courtesy, so don't be surprised if you are in an area of heavy boat traffic and hear a Coastie break in on a hail from one boat to another and remind them to use Channel 09 for boat-to-boat hailing.

VHF Radio Channel Etiquette

You may have heard a boater who talks too long and too often on the radio. Besides being annoying, that person is tying up the channel so no one else can use it. Transmissions should be brief and to the point. Wait your turn or seek another channel. Unless there is an emergency, never walk over another conversation by interrupting it.

It's also important to speak clearly and slowly into the microphone. Take your time, and you will not have to repeat yourself. This advice applies equally to those of us who are excited about long-time-no-see boating friends, as well as those of us who might find ourselves out of fuel and need help quickly. Calm down, speak slowly, clearly, and get the message out correctly the first time.

*****

THERE IS NO PRIVACY ON A VHF RADIO! When you switch from Channel 16 to a working channel, remember that anyone on the same channel can hear your conversation. This excerpt from Escape from the Ordinary, one of my books about sailing around the world, paints an excellent picture of the public nature of radio communications and the importance of knowing which channel to use.

Whatever meaning the term party line may have today, it originally described a non-private arrangement of sharing one telephone line between two or more houses. Each house serviced by the party line could join or listen to what other speaking parties probably believed a private call. Boat radios are similar, except the communication is over a marine VHF radio that anyone within about 12 miles tuned to a particular channel can hear. At sea, boats keep the VHF radio on channel 16, the international hailing and distress channel, but at anchor in remote areas, the radio becomes a way for cruisers to chat with other boats.

If you are at anchor and want to announce a fish grill and potluck on the beach, you can spread the word to other boats on what cruising sailors sometimes call the **chat channels**—in this case channel 67. If you want to converse with a particular friend on a nearby boat, you call them on channel 67 and ask the person to switch to another undesignated **private** channel of your mutual choosing. Depending upon what is happening, it's likely any boat that hears you—and every villager ashore with a VHF radio—would follow you to the *private* channel to listen in on the conversation. We learned something important during a conversation between sailors on S/V *Lollipop* and S/V *Sailing Home* through such a call.

"Lollipop, Lollipop, *this is* Sailing Home, *over.*"

"Lollipop, *here.*"

"Lollipop, *switch to channel 63.*"

Lollipop and almost everyone else switched to Channel 63:

"What's up, Sailing Home?"

"Did you hear what happened to Dragonfly*? It just got towed back yesterday by a local boat. The owners had to pay thousands of dollars to get it back."*

"Whoa! Tell me everything from the beginning."

"The owners of Dragonfly *dropped anchor and left for a day ashore. They hired a car to see the volcanic ruins of St. Pierre and hike the Beauregard Canal. The wind picked up while they were gone, and they didn't have enough anchor chain out for the winds and steep bottom. Their boat dragged anchor and floated out to sea. The owners returned just before nightfall and freaked out when they got back, and their boat was gone. They thought someone had stolen it, so they went to the police station. The French gendarmes told them,*

68

"*No one steals 50-foot sailboats around here—this is France. It probably dragged anchor. It's happened before.*"

The French police put the word out on 16 (the distress channel) that a sailboat was drifting around. It was too dark to find a missing boat, but an islander motored out at daybreak, found the vessel, and claimed it as salvage. The islander found a key in the ignition, started the sailboat engine, and towed his small fishing boat back. The islander demanded $100,000 to return the boat. The couple accused him of stealing the boat and got the police involved—a real mess. The police ended up helping with a settlement. The owners paid a few thousand dollars finder's fee in the end. They are lucky this is a French island—on some others, the finders might have been keepers. End of story."

Without the slightest bit of embarrassment about eavesdropping, other boats broke in and started asking questions and conjecturing about international salvage laws. The channel got crowded with comments, and I turned back to the hailing channel. Glen and I talked about what had happened. Could someone claim your boat if the anchor dragged, it floated out to sea, and no one was aboard? Concerned, we played it safe and let out a more extended scope of anchor chain to accommodate for the steep and deep ocean floor. Glen powered in reverse to set the anchor securely for good measure, and we waved to other sailors on deck doing the same.

From eavesdropping I learned a variety of helpful information, including: there was a car rental place in town, an erupting volcano had once destroyed Martinique, one could hike the Beauregard Canal, and we should lengthen our anchor chain to compensate for the sloping ocean floor.

NOTE: The above conversation violated some rules we talk about below. When you are cruising internationally, you will notice that your VHF radio becomes a combination lifesaving tool and cellphone substitute.

*****

FUN FACT: In the United States, you do not need a radio license to operate a VHF radio. In many other countries, you do.

Channel Guide

Hailing occurs on 16, right? Or 09? Why won't that bridge tender answer my call on 16? What channel do I use to hail a bridge tender? How do I pick a working channel to switch to after the party I am trying to reach responds?

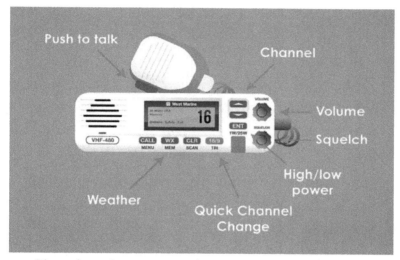

Choosing the correct channel can be a little more complicated than it first appears, but the confusion will soon disappear with just a little review. Let's go for it!

VHF Channel Rules

Every channel on VHF radio has a specific purpose. For recreational boaters and sailors in U.S. waters, these are the most used channels:

Channel 16

As you know by now, Channel 16 is the designated international hailing and distress channel. This channel should always be on and monitored—while you are underway and at anchor, too. You should not use this for casual conversation and or even comms check in busy boating areas. If you do, you could (without even knowing it) be preventing someone from reaching help in a disaster.

U.S. Coast Guard rules state, "In general, any vessel equipped with a VHF marine radio…must maintain a watch on *channel 16* (156.800 MHz) whenever the radio is not being used to communicate."

On crowded summer weekends, you may hear a periodic announcement over the VHF from the U.S. Coast Guard:

"Please be advised that due to a high volume of calls channel 16 is not a hailing frequency, it is presently reserved for emergency use only."

In busy waters, especially weekends, don't be that person asking for a radio check or having a conversation with your buddy on 16. Switch to a working channel and hold your conversation there. If you need a radio check, channel 09 is where you start.

If there is emergency activity occurring on channel 16, stay off the radio unless you can offer specific help to the situation. Boaters should hold all routine radio hailing and standby when emergency traffic takes place on channel 16.

*NOTE: The more remote your anchorage, the more critical it is to **monitor channel 16 even at anchor and overnight.** In secluded anchorages, we become each other's safety net. Be an asset to the local boating community by keeping your radio on channel 16 even after successfully anchoring and turning in for the night.*

Should you be at anchor or in a marina slip when a stiff blow comes through, turn your radio on to monitor channel Calls of vessels dragging at anchor—some occupied and some perhaps not—will come on 16, along with calls for assistance or reports of dinghies and other items that have broken free and not under control in the anchorage.

Monitoring channel 16 is your contribution to helping keep the boating community around you safe and secure. You may just be the help that someone else needs.

*****

Just one of many reasons you should monitor channel 16 at night when docked or anchored:

Boaters tied their boats to a town wall on the Illinois River. During the night someone from town boarded a few of the twelve boats and removed the mooring lines from both the boat and shoreside. One captain woke up and shouted the alarm on Channel 16 so the other boaters could start their engines to avoid hitting a bridge downstream and going aground. The first untied boats floated down the river as the owners slept below decks. The boats with their VHF radio turned on heard the call, woke up and took command of the situation, but boats with radios off found out the hard way. Ouch!

The moral of the story is to keep your VHF radio on channel 16 when at anchor or docked. Dodgy situations pop up when you least expect them.

*****

- **Channel 16**: For hailing, safety, and emergency use, only.
- **Channel 09**: Pleasure-boat hailing channel.
- **Channels 68, 69, 71, 72,** and **78A**: Recreational working channels used for boat-to-boat traffic.
- **Channels 1, 7A, 8, 10, 11, 18A, 19A, 63, 77, 79A, 80A,** and **88A**: Commercial channels (pleasure boaters are supposed to stay off them).

- **Channel 13**: For requesting bridge openings, although, in some areas, it's channel 09 or 67. Consult your cruising guide or *Active Captain* notes on your electronic charts.
- Channels 24, 25, 26, 27, 28, 84, 85, 86 and 87: Used by marine operators.
- **Channel 22A**: Coast Guard working channel where they make safety broadcasts after alerting you on channel 16 and asking you to switch over.
- **Channel 06**: For inter-ship safety and search and rescue communications. Used exclusively by the ships and aircraft of the Coast Guard.
- **Channels 1, 5, 12, 14, 20, 63, 65A, 66A, 73, 74 and 77**: For port operations. Available to recreational boats in areas where no port operations exist.
- **Channel 70**: A digital channel dedicated to Digital Selective Calling (DSC). DSC is an automated distress system that allows us to make digital phone calls through our VHFs. It's not illegal to make voice calls on Channel 70—it's not possible. (See: *Is your VHF set up correctly?*)

*****

Don't try to memorize everything before you hold that mic in your hand for the first time. Like everything else, a little practice is a key to understanding all the ins and outs. Before you get underway, try listening to conversations on various channels to familiarize yourself with radio lingo and keep a channel guide handy to help you out in the beginning. Listening to others' techniques, you may hear a few calls that don't exactly go by the book and can learn a lot from those calls.

Can boats with American radios talk to someone using a Canadian-programmed radio?

Yes. Rarely will you encounter difficulties communicating with vessel operators who are using radios from Canada or elsewhere worldwide. This difference is apt to occur when you are on a channel followed by the letter A, which indicates you are on a **duplex channel**.

On VHF radios programmed for North America, the most common duplex channel is 22A, the Coast Guard Maritime Safety Information channel. The United States Coast Guard and Canadian Coast Guard share 22A for special weather and safety messages.

Keep in mind that if you have issues contacting someone return to 16 or your agreed-hailing channel such as 09 and reestablish contact. From there, you can move to simplex or non-duplex working channels such as 68, 69, 71, and 72.

*****

FUN FACT: During the early days of radio, those in the vicinity of a powerful radio station in Cincinnati, Ohio could hear the audio in their pans, pots, and mattresses.

CHAPTER 6

Radio Lingo

Radio lingo evolved from military communications, often under challenging conditions and as a matter of life or death. It is more likely your message will get through and be understood by using these standard phrases and protocol and keeping your messages short. This is especially important when there is an emergency on your boat.

Stay calm and be clear in your day-to-day radio communications and it will serve you well in an emergency. Whenever you're transmitting—emergency or otherwise—speak slowly and distinctly, one word at a time. Keep the mic an inch or so away from your mouth and try to shelter yourself from the wind.

In this chapter, we will learn about words and spelling over the VHF radio, including:

- Useful terms and Prowords
- Words and phrases to avoid

- How to spell using the phonetic alphabet

*****

There are many reasons to keep your boat name short and easy to understand but spelling it phonetically over the radio is the most significant. Long, difficult names such as *Winter is Coming* and *Sir Ossis of the River* are difficult to understand over the airways and so unusual others will likely ask you to spell it phonetically. If this sounds daunting, stay tuned, I have a fun and easy tip for practicing until you know the phonetic alphabet by heart.

*****

Prowords—Key to Clarity

The Coast Guard is an arm of the military and they deploy worldwide on their vessels and aboard Navy ships. My husband and I were surprised to occasionally run across the US Coast Guard in far off waters off the Horn of Africa, Indian Ocean and South America. To speak with the US Coast Guard as well as their foreign equivalents, you must speak in a standard format using procedure words and the international phonetic alphabet.

Short for procedure words, **prowords** convey information in a standardized format initially developed by the military and now known worldwide. Prowords are what the pros use and making friends with them will ensure your time on the airwaves is enjoyable and effective—but don't take it to extremes. Your goal is to communicate effectively, not sound like a Special Forces commando or police officer.

Using unfamiliar or nonstandard phrases can confuse conversations and cause unnecessary delays in emergencies. If you plan to sail international waters, the following specific phrases or words will make it easier when you need to talk over the radio to a foreign immigration or customs officer who does not speak English. Learn the following terms, and you will be well on your way to pro.

Useful Terms and Prowords

- **Affirmative**. Yes. Affirmative is easier to understand over the radio than simply saying, "Yes."
- **Negative**. No. It is also much easier to understand.
- **Roger**. Received, or I understand.
- **Copy**. I received your message.
- **Over**. You have finished talking and await a reply. Avoid using this unless it is necessary. Pausing at the logical end of your part of a two-

way conversation is usually sufficient. You should only say "over" at the end of a transmission compromised due to distance or other factors such as noise.

- **Out**. You are finished talking, and do not expect a reply. Unlike Hollywood, we do not use "over and out" together.
- **Clear**. You are leaving a channel or turning your radio off.
- **Say again**. Repeat the last transmission.
- **Say again all after [a specific word]**. Repeat your last transmission beginning when the person said a specific word or phrase.
- **Stand by**. Directs the listener to hold on a moment. It is commonly used after receiving a question that requires a moment's thought or time to look up something before replying. For example, if *S/V Skimmer* asks me the coordinates of a good anchorage, I will need to look at the chart and respond with, "Stand by, *Skimmer*," while I retrieve the coordinates.
- **Standing by**. You have finished your conversation but will remain to monitor this or another channel. For example, "*Star Dust*, standing by on zero-nine."

A Few Don'ts

- **10-4**. Say "affirmative." Leave 10-4 to the truckers.
- **CB Lingo**. Do not use CB or police radio lingo.
- **Over**. Over made both lists, because it is very effective to use when necessary, and good to avoid when not. It is annoying to hear "over" after every crisp, clear sentence.
- **Come back**. Avoid this. Make your call, and then wait. Asking, "Are you out there?" or adding, "come on back" after transmission is annoying and clogs the airwaves.
- **Profanity**. Never. Keep it off the airwaves.
- **Music**. It is against the law to transmit music over a VHF.
- **Children**. Teach children proper, responsible VHF radio use and etiquette. Let them know your radio is not for entertainment or karaoke. Never allow young children to play with any part of your VHF radio.

Phonetic Alphabet

If you are spelling something on the radio, some letters sound much alike (i.e., B, D, G, T, V, A). If we all made up a spelling language, we would run into folks hearing, "T as in toy," when what we said was, "B as in boy." It would cause unnecessary confusion. To overcome this problem, an international communications organization worked with the military to devise an official phonetic alphabet for radio communication.

Phonetic or 'Spelling' Alphabet

A	Alfa	N	November
B	Bravo	O	Oscar
C	Charlie	P	Papa
D	Delta	Q	Quebec
E	Echo	R	Romeo
F	Foxtrot	S	Sierra
G	Golf	T	Tango
H	Hotel	U	Uniform
I	India	V	Victor
J	Juliett	W	Whiskey
K	Kilo	X	X-ray
L	Lima	Y	Yankee
M	Mike	Z	Zulu

NOTE: I have not misspelled Alfa and Juliett. They are spelled in this way to avoid pronunciation confusion among international users.

Anyone who has ever watched a war movie has heard the phonetic alphabet in use. Professionals use these easily understandable words rather than a letter when they need to ensure the information is clearly understood. For example, you may have heard them use alfa for the letter A, bravo for the letter B, and so on.

Always use the phonetic alphabet to transmit something important such as a location or your boat name. It is the most powerful way to be understood the first time. Post a copy of the phonetic alphabet next to your radio until you have it memorized. Numbers should always be digital, "seven-two," for example, instead of "seventy-two." Pronounce numbers in the usual manner, except for "nine," which you pronounce "niner." To ensure international understanding, you must use these specific words. Here's the complete phonetic alphabet.

Don't be surprised if folks on land use the phonetic alphabet. When the marina dockmaster assigns you to slip *Mike 8*, look for a sign displaying M8; Hotel 7 is H7. Like every aspect of radio communication, it becomes second nature if you use it enough. You can find copies of this table to download online.

TIP: An excellent way to practice the phonetic alphabet is by saying the letters of the licenses plate of the car ahead of you while you are driving.

Your boat's name is the most common thing you will spell over the radio, so commit those phonetic replacements to memory first. Consider printing and laminating it onto a small card and posting it by the radio or remote access microphone. Our former boat, *Star Dust*, sounds like this over the radio:

"**S**ierra **T**ango **A**lfa **R**omeo, new word, **D**elta **U**niform **S**ierra **T**ango."

With every boat, we select a name that makes it easier to spell phonetically over the radio. Our latest, based in Mexico, means the same thing in both English and Spanish: *Escape:*

"**E**cho, **S**ierra, **C**harlie, **A**lfa, **P**apa, **E**cho."

Just for fun, phonetically spell out the names of your family members, pets, and your boat name. If you don't have a boat yet, spell out the make and model of your dream boat. Perhaps that will help bring it to life!

*****

During the morning cruising net, there is often a section that welcomes new arrivals to the anchorage. One morning, the net controller asked a new arrival with a heavy Scottish accent to spell the name of his sailboat *S/V Enterprise*. The captain did not know the official phonetic alphabet, so he created his own.

E as in Elephant

N as in Niagara—the one in Canada T as in tangerine

E as in (here he hesitated not wanting to use Elephant twice) Egg

R as in Roger P as in Petrol R as in Ronny I as in Ice

S as in Sugar

E as in (hesitates again but goes with) Elephant.

It was difficult to keep from laughing, especially at the clarification of which side of Niagara Falls he meant. Don't let your fellow boaters have a great joke at your expense! Memorize and practice the international phonetic alphabet.

*****

FUN FACT: Radio waves from your VHF antenna transmit through the air via line of sight. The signal can only travel through the air if there is no obstruction, such as a forest, mountain, or tall buildings. However, more sophisticated radios exist, transmitting on extremely low frequencies through the ground to submarines in distant oceans. Electrodes placed in the ground miles apart use the earth's core as a giant antenna to transmit radio signals to submarines trailing long underwater antennas.

AUTHOR'S NOTE: While sailing the Chesapeake Bay near Norfolk, I changed course to avoid what looked like a pole sticking out of the water, though I could not see it indicated on the chart. As a submarine

emerged from the depths, I realized the pole had been a periscope checking to make sure it could surface without hitting another boat. What I could not see was whether there was a very long antenna trailing behind.

*****

The phonetic alphabet is mostly a memorization exercise. Depending on your memory skills, it could take you as little as an hour or as much as several hours over a couple of weeks to get it locked in.

My suggestions:

1. Write out a copy (yes, old fashioned pen and paper) to help remember each word.

2. Recite the list in order several times

3. Use it to spell out words, referencing your list as required. You can use any printed material such as a newspaper, book, or magazine as your source of words.

4. Repeat step 3 without peeking at the list. Note any words you keep forgetting and look them up at the end of the exercise. Repeat the process and focus on these few.

5. Leave it for a day or two. Try step 4 again. Focus on relearning the ones you forgot.

6. Repeat step 5 as required until you have firmly established the International Phonetic Alphabet in your memory.

You will be glad you memorized the phonetic alphabet during an emergency when time is critical, and things are happening fast.

CHAPTER 7

Emergency Calls

Everyone who owns or crews on a boat needs to be able to both make and respond to a distress call over the VHF radio. **The Three Types of Voice (non-automated) Emerg**ency Calls:

- Mayday
- PAN-PAN
- Sécurité

In addition to emergency calls, there are emergency radio relays. We will cover these as well:

- Emergency relays
- How and when to offer an emergency relay call

NOTE: This section is voice calls. Modern VHF radios also have automated Digital Selective Calling (DSC) and can be programmed to make an emergency call with the push of a button. You will learn how to set it up and use DSC in the Advanced Radio Features section. However, even if your radio has DSC capabilities, it is essential to understand how to make a voice emergency call. Your base unit radio may be damaged, or you could be on a boat with an older VHF radio that lacks digital functions. In foreign waters there may not be a Coast Guard monitoring DSC and a voice call may be your only option.

Emergency calls are the most critical traffic on channel 16—because of their life-and-death nature, you must follow a specific communications protocol. If you boat is going down, you may only have time for one emergency call. Knowing and rehearsing what to say ahead of time will ensure that your call, should you need to make one, will bring assistance as soon as possible.

From highest to lowest priority:

Mayday—*Mayday* comes from the French word *m'aidez* for *help me*. Mayday indicates you are in a life-threatening emergency and require immediate assistance from the Coast Guard or any mariner who can assist.

Let's clarify when to call a Mayday—the call a vessel makes when there is an immediate and present risk to the vessel or the lives aboard it. This distress may include situations such as a capsized vessel, a boat taking on dangerous amounts of water, or life-threatening injury or illness to the crew. Mayday tells the Coast Guard and other vessels to drop everything and come to your rescue.

Should you find yourself in this kind of danger, follow these steps to make an effective Mayday call.

Steps to Making a Mayday Call

1. On channel 16, key your mic and repeat "Mayday" three times. Be sure to speak clearly and deliberately. Do not shout or rush.

    "Mayday. Mayday. Mayday."

2. Identify yourself. This information should include your boat's name and a straightforward visual description.

    "This is the sailing vessel New Latitude. *We are 40-feet long with a white hull. Our sails are down."*

3. Give your location. Practice finding and calling out your GPS coordinates. If these coordinates are not available, be as precise as you can. Avoid vague terms such as "near the inlet" or "just off the estuary."

    "We are located at twenty-four degrees, fifty-seven minutes, north by eighty-two degrees, ten minutes, west, on the western side of the Marquesas Keys."

4. Briefly describe your emergency. Don't tell the back story of how it happened. Time is critical. Just describe your emergency.

    "We have hit a reef. Our hull is punctured, and we are taking on a lot of water."

5. Provide the number of people on board. Be sure to say if some of these are children or if anyone is injured.

    "There are four souls aboard: Two adults, a 10-year old, and an 8-year old. One of the adults is injured. She fell down the companionway when we hit the reef and broke her leg. No other injuries."

6. Let them know when you have completed relaying your information.

    "Over."

If you have a crew onboard, assign one member to make and receive radio calls during your emergency. Avoid the confusion of multiple people on and off the radio. Remember, you must monitor channel 16 after making your Mayday call—the call itself is only part of the equation. The critical next step is being available, calm, and ready to respond to those trying to help.

The U.S. Coast Guard jumps into action when you make a Mayday call. They direct massive resources across long distances to get to you as soon as possible—

regardless of the risk and the cost. Therefore, everyone must reserve Maydays for genuinely life-threatening situations. Examples include:

- A non-contained fire aboard
- A capsized boat
- A vessel caught in stormy weather and taking on water
- A life-threatening medical emergency such as a heart attack or significant injury
- A sinking boat or one taking on more water than it can pump overboard.

Here is another example of a well-executed Mayday call:

"Mayday, Mayday, Mayday. This is the motorboat Good Catch, Good Catch, Good Catch, *MMSI 232000111."*

(You'll learn about the MMSI number in Advanced Functions.)

"Mayday. Good Catch. *MMSI 232000111. My position is 24.6333°N, 82.9200°W. Fire onboard. Require immediate assistance. Six souls on board. Abandoning to dinghy. Over."*

This information gets the Coast Guard on the way or allows any nearby Good Samaritan boater to help until the Coast Guard arrives.

NOTE: The term souls avoids the confusion of a captain giving the number of passengers aboard and not including himself or the crew.

If the Coast Guard wishes to work the emergency on channel 16, it will declare, "silence Mayday" (pronounced *see-lonce*, from the French version). At this point, all other traffic on channel 16 must cease until the Coast Guard releases the channel. When the Coast Guard reopens the channel, it will declare "*silence fini*" (*fin-ee*) or "silence prudence" (*pru-donce*). Anyone other than the Coast Guard seeking to keep a channel clear for emergency communications should call "silence distress" (*see-lonce*).

Some people use MIPDANIO to remember the order of the Mayday message. Make a copy of this format that includes your MMSI number, if your radio is so equipped, to keep at the radio.

M – Mayday

I – Identification

P – Position

D – Distress type

A – Assistance required

N – Number of people on board

I – Information (additional information to relay such as abandoning to life raft, drifting east at 3 knots, no dinghy or liferaft aboard,one passenger is diabetic, etc.).

O – Over.

PAN-PAN—(pronounced *pawn-pawn* from the French word *panne,* which means *breakdown*) indicates a potentially life-threatening emergency you would like others to monitor until you resolve the situation. PAN-PAN applies to an urgent situation that, for the time being, does not pose an immediate threat to one's life. In some cases, people making Mayday calls should instead be making PAN-PAN calls.

A PAN-PAN call follows the same steps as a Mayday call, except you start the call with "PAN-PAN."

Should you find yourself in an urgent, but not life-threatening situation that you are working to resolve, follow these steps to make an effective PAN-PAN call.

1. On channel 16, key your mic and repeat "PAN-PAN" three times. Be sure to speak clearly and deliberately. Do not shout or rush.

   "PAN-PAN, PAN-PAN, PAN-PAN."

2. Identify yourself. This should include your boat's name as well as a very simple visual description.

   "This is motor vessel Luna. We are a 38-foot white hulled motor yacht."

3. Give your location. Practice finding and calling out your GPS coordinates.

"We are located at 24 degrees 55 minutes north by 82 degrees 17 minutes west."

4. Briefly describe your emergency. Just describe what your emergency is.

   "We are taking on water after going aground. We have found the source of the problem and working to fix it. For now, the bilge pump is working and keeping the level down to a few inches of water. We do not have a liferaft or dinghy. Would appreciate if the Coast Guard or any boat within the sound of this call can come to our assistance if we can't fix the problem."

5. Tell how many people are onboard. Be sure to say if some of these are children or if anyone is injured.

   "There are four adults and one 3-year-old child on board. We are not injured."

6. Say "over" when you have completed relaying your information.

   "Over."

Your PAN-PAN call will start a conversation with the Coast Guard about their level of response.

Situations when a PAN-PAN call is appropriate:

- Fouled propeller, engine failure, or out of fuel. The crew may plan to clear the propeller, refuel from an onboard supply, hoist sail, or use alternative propulsion. Use a PAN-PAN call if the vessel is safe from any immediate danger of collision or stranding. As part of the PAN-PAN call, the skipper may request a tow from a suitable vessel in the area, if possible.

- **Small fire on board, now extinguished**. An onboard fire is serious, but a PAN-PAN call is appropriate if it was small, contained, put out, and there were no injuries. Your call warns others to be aware of the situation. After the call, assess the extent of the damage, clear the smoke from below, and re-establish passage as soon as possible.

- **Urgent accident or medical situation** that may escalate and require outside assistance.

- **Taking on water**. A broken fitting has caused an influx of water into the boat that your bilge pump can handle while you make repairs at sea. Unsure if your bilge pump can keep up while you make the repair, you request monitoring of your situation by the Coast Guard and request any nearby boater to stay close in case it becomes a Mayday situation.

- **Man-overboard recovery**. If you have a man overboard situation, have that person in sight, and are maneuvering to recover that person, a

PAN-PAN call on VHF makes other nearby vessels aware of the problem, ensures that they keep a lookout, avoid coming too close, and limit their wake or otherwise interfere. It also alerts them that the recovery vessel is maneuvering for urgent lifesaving, and therefore may not act according to area regulations. In a more critical situation where the recovery vessel has lost sight of the person overboard, the person overboard is unconscious, and there is a danger of hypothermia or another risk to life, a Mayday call is more appropriate, so nearby vessels can help rather than keep clear.

Sécurité

Sécurité (pronounced *si-CURE-it-TAY*) is the least urgent of the three distress and urgency calls. Sécurité is usually a radio call that announces navigational warnings, such as a towboat bringing a disabled vessel into an inlet or riverway, a boat entering a blind, narrow passage, or an announcement about something adrift that represents a hazard to boaters in the area.

The U.S. Coast Guard often makes sécurité announcements, usually about waterway hazards. However, I have heard sécurité broadcast from a tugboat captain piloting other vessels as well as a towboat working to free a freighter that had gone aground. Learn to listen to these and write down the relayed information and grid coordinates for reference.

Emergency Relays

Let's hope you never have to relay or ask another boater to relay a Mayday call, but you will know how after this section.

A radio relay passes a message from its source through at least one go-between and then to its final destination. Although not very common, relays are essential, especially during an emergency.

If you hear a boat making an emergency call (Mayday or PAN-PAN) and no one is answering them, you should first respond to the vessel making the call to let them know you heard their call. If you are not able to come to their aid, let them know you will relay or rebroadcast their information. Performing this service allows a longer reach for the 20 mile or so range of their VHF radio, gives the distressed crew a chance to work on their problem, and saves their batteries. Contact the Coast Guard for them on channel 16 with the relay procedure described below.

In emergencies, be sure you write down all the details (boat name, nature of emergency, and location), and then put out your call on high power on channel 16.

Here are examples of situations that show the importance of relays in distress situations.

You are sailing on S/V *Shooting Star* and hear M/V *Eclipse* send a Mayday, but no one has acknowledged the distress communication.

You note all the details and wait three minutes before transmitting the following message. You include your details (you are on S/V *Shooting Star*), but the message is a carbon copy of M/V *Eclipse*'s message.

"Mayday relay, Mayday relay, Mayday relay.

This is sailing vessel Shooting Star, Shooting Star, Shooting Star. *MMSI 232000000.*

Mayday Motor Vessel Eclipse. MMSI 234000000.

In position 24.63°N, 82.92°W.

Holed and sinking.

Require immediate assistance.

Three souls on board.

They have no liferaft.

Over."

Here is a different type of situation. In this example, you are sending a message on behalf of an unknown person, so details are either unknown or not needed. In this case, you just do your best (you are on S/V *Shooting Star*).

"Mayday relay, Mayday relay, Mayday relay.

This is sailing vessel Shooting Star. *MMSI 235890000.*

Mayday.

Stranded person at base of cliff.

Approximate position 45.25°N 69.44°W.

He has been cut off by tide—partially immersed in water. Immediate assistance required.

Over."

If you do not receive a reply within a minute, repeat your call and ask if anyone can hear and give another relay. Relays are often required when a boater in distress has a lower-powered handheld VHF that does not transmit as far as strong base station units.

Your Duty to Assist

The centuries old tradition of mariners coming to each other's aid is also called the *Good Samaritan Law.*

You are obligated to relay emergency calls and, if it appears you are in the best position to render aid, take what further action you are able, without endangering your boat or crew.

Each year, many on-the-water emergencies are assisted by good Samaritans who arrive on the scene before Coast Guard rescue crews. Never assume that someone else will handle a Mayday call. If you hear an unanswered call, get on the radio, acknowledge the Mayday, boat name, its location, nature of distress, and then use the procedure listed above to relay the Mayday to the Coast Guard.

I have heard this scenario played out. A boat 100 miles out experiences an emergency and a boat closer to shore acts as a communications bridge, transmitting critical information from the vessel in distress to the Coast Guard and vice versa.

If a Mayday call is issued offshore and you are within range, immediately head for the location of the emergency. A friend had a sailboat sink under him, sent out a Mayday as the boat went down, and a nearby trawler immediately steamed a few miles to his location, rescuing him and his crew. A center console fishing boat in the Sea of Cortez had an electrical fire 20 miles offshore. The crew abandoned ship due to the smoke and flames but were immediately saved by other fishing boats who responded quickly to the Mayday call.

However, there are times when circumstances do not allow you to do more than perform communications relay. Besides the actual mechanics of the radio call, you must use your judgment when deciding what level of assistance is safe for you and your crew. Circumstances such as wind, waves, weather, capability of your own boat and experience of your crew will influence your decision.

Here is an emergency situation where my husband and I were faced with analyzing all those factors and making that difficult decision.

Mayday in the South Pacific

Halfway through a sail passage between New Zealand and Fiji, the wind was 30 knots, gusting to 40 and our ketch was making 6 kts under reefed sails. Seas had built to 10 – 12-feet. Alone on night watch, I was using radar returns to navigate around the more intense squalls and my husband was off watch, sleeping below. The wind in the rigging made so much noise I barely heard the crackle of the VHF radio on Channel 16.

"Mayday. Mayday, Mayday.

This is the sailboat Ocean Highway.

My location is 27.168 S, 178.98E.

I have lost steerage. The mainsheet is wrapped around my prop, and the boat is beam to the waves. My wife is dehydrated from seasickness and needs medical assistance.

Asking for rescue from any ship within the sound of my voice.

I repeat, Mayday, Mayday, Mayday.

This is sailboat Ocean Highway...*"*

The first rule of responding to a distress call is grab pen and paper and write down what you hear. The distress vessel may only be able to get out one call and you want to capture all the information possible the first time. Our fixed base VHF radio was below decks at the navigation station, with a notebook handy. Before responding to the call, I wrote down everything I heard, then woke my husband, and asked him to plot the grid coordinates while I called back to the distressed vessel on Channel 16. Once plotted, we saw that the boat in trouble was 25 miles behind us, at the extreme edge of the range of a VHF radio antenna. We adjusted course to tack back to their location.

"Ocean Highway, *this is sailing vessel* It's Enough.

We are 25 miles N/NE of your position.

Are you abandoning ship because you are taking on water?"

"It's Enough, *this is* Ocean Highway.

Not sinking but sideway to the waves. Somehow the knot came out in the main sheet and when we tacked it spun out and wrapped around the prop. Then I tried to start the engine and the line wrapped even tighter around the prop. I can't motor or sail now. I'm not a diver. Can you help us? We need to abandon this boat. I would deploy our life raft, but it hasn't been serviced in years. Plus my wife is seasick, the waves are big and not sure we could handle it in these seas. Please come pick us up and take us wherever you are heading."

At this point another sailboat is asking us to risk our life and boat in high wind and seas for a situation that sounds very uncomfortable but can get sorted out when the weather clears. Abandoning a floating boat for a life raft, especially in raging seas, is never a good idea. As for coming alongside another sailboat in storm conditions, the masts and rigging could entangle, dismasting both boats. Considering the wind, waves and that their boat was not in danger of sinking, we decided it was too dangerous to attempt rescue, especially in the middle of the night.

Law of the Sea Rule Number Two is Do No Harm to yourself or the vessel in distress.

Instead of a rescue we offered to stand by and relay their Mayday to any ship or Coast Guard that might be within our own radio range.

"Ocean Highway, Ocean Highway *this is sailing vessel* It's Enough.*"*

"Ocean Highway *here."*

"Ocean Highway, *this is* It's Enough. *We are a crew of two about 25 miles north of your position. Unable to render assistance in this storm but will stay within VHF range to relay your call and stay close by until help arrives. Ocean Highway, what is the length and color of your hull? Which direction are you drifting, and what is the MMSI number of your boat? We are not picking up your AIS on our VHF radio (explained in Advanced Functions section) Over."*

"It's Enough *this is* Ocean Highway. *Our hull is white, and we are 42-feet long. We have an old radio. No MMSI or AIS. We are drifting east at around three knots. Over."*

We tacked to keep *It's Enough* within VHF range and began transmitting a Mayday relay call to extend the reach of *Ocean Highway's* VHF radio and save his battery. **It is important to announce that you are performing a *relay* and that it is not your boat in distress**.

"Mayday Relay, Mayday Relay, Mayday Relay, all stations, all stations, all stations, this is S/V It's Enough, It's Enough, It's Enough. Mayday S/V Ocean Highway, Ocean Highway, Ocean Highway, approximately 27.168 S, 178.98 E. S/V Ocean Highway has lost steerage and propulsion with a sick crew member. Requests immediate assistance. Two persons on board. White hulled sailboat, drifting east by at least three knots from grid coordinates. Over."

Within an hour our Mayday relay call was picked up by a passing ship. *"It's Enough,* this is the *Evergreen* container ship heading for Australia. What is the nature of the emergency for the boat in distress?"

"M/V Evergreen *this is S/V* It's Enough. *I am relaying a Mayday call for S/V* Ocean Highway *who has lost steerage, propulsion, and use of their mainsail. The skipper wants to abandon ship. Their location is approximately 27.168 S 178.98 E Are you able to render assistance?"*

"It's Enough, It's Enough, *M/V* Evergreen. *Let* Ocean Highway *know we are willing to attempt in these conditions but will pull away if it looks like we will run them down coming alongside. We are 260-feet long, and they must be able to climb 40 feet up the side of our ship on a net ladder. If they deem their situation life threatening, we can be there in two hours. Will attempt to form a barrier between them and the storm to come alongside. If they can make it aboard, our next port is Brisbane. Over."*

I called *Ocean Highway* and let them know a 260-foot-long container ship was willing to divert course and attempt a rescue.

"Ocean Highway, Ocean Highway, *this is* It's Enough. *The 260-foot-long container ship* Evergreen *is willing to attempt a rescue if able in these conditions. They will make that decision when they arrive your location. Are you and your wife able to climb 40 feet up a rope ladder in storm conditions? Over.*"

"It's Enough, *ask Evergreen if they can send someone down to help my wife. She can hardly stand.*"

At that point M/V *Evergreen* was close enough to communicate and broke in to speak directly with *Ocean Highway*.

"*Break, Break.* Ocean Highway *this is M/V* Evergreen. *Your signal is weak but readable. How do you read me?*"

"Evergreen *this is* Ocean Highway. *I hear you fine.*"

From that point the two vessels communicated directly with each other. M/V *Evergreen's* VHF antenna was mounted high on a tall ship, so their side of the radio communication traveled far beyond normal VHF range. Hours after the first distress call the captain of the M/V Evergreen instructed S/V *Ocean Highway* skipper to be ready to go when they pulled the ship along the windward side, creating a lee in the wind and waves.

Monitoring Channel 16 we listened as a seaman from the *Evergreen* climbed down a rope ladder to assist the crew of *Ocean Highway* up the side of the ship in high wind and seas. The sailboat was then abandoned, left floating as a hazard to navigation in the Pacific Ocean.

NOTE: The Coast Guard normally scuttles (sinks) abandoned boats so that they are not hazards to the safe navigation of other boats. An abandoned boat is likely to eventually collide with another vessel at night or break up when it hits a reef or shore.

Non-Emergency Relays

Thankfully, most relays you give are a courtesy rather than an emergency. Here is a common situation: You can hear two boats clearly, but they have problems hearing each other; you may be between them. When this happens, it's nice to offer a relay.

"Break. [Wait for the two speakers to pause, then say both boats' names].

This is M/V Star Dust. *I can hear you both clearly. Would you like a relay?"*

If they say yes, direct everyone to a working channel you have already checked to make sure it is clear, such as channel 68, 69, 71, or 72.

If someone offers to relay for you, keep your conversation as short as possible. Be clear and concise, as opportunities for miscommunication are even greater going through a third person. Relays are an essential part of boating life. Be aware and be prepared to offer aid if it is needed.

*****

Example of boaters pitching in to help:

A lady on channel 16 called for help but was not using the word Mayday. Close to hysterics, she said her husband had fallen overboard, he was injured, and she could not get him back on the boat. She did throw a line to him, so at least she knew where he was. However, the woman had no idea where **she** was, and her husband had been using the electronic charts and GPS on his smart phone, which was in his pocket. The Coast Guard was not responding, so other boaters jumped in to figure out her location by asking where she lived, what roads they took to the marina, what she could see, etc...

After about 20 minutes, someone figured out where she was from all the clues and headed her way. The panicked lady then said, "Do you think I should stop the boat; my husband is having a hard time hanging on." She had been dragging him along behind the boat the whole time! Everyone on the radio keyed up and said, "*YES!*"

Soon after, a fellow boater arrived and helped get her husband back on the boat. Shortly after that, the Coast Guard came, took the guy to the hospital, and helped his wife get the boat tied up.

Be sure to train your crew to operate the GPS, use the VHF radio and make a Mayday call. Also, how to stop the boat!

When to Use a Cell Phone

A smartphone loaded with electronic charts and weather prediction apps is an important tool for mariners. However, for an emergency in U.S. waters, always contact the U.S. Coast Guard on channel 16 of your VHF radio. Almost always, your marine VHF radio is better than a cell phone on the water. Radios have better battery life and do not rely on cell towers for connection. Also, remember that broadcasting a Mayday over Channel 16 of your VHF radio allows you to reach all boaters within the range of your radio. There may be a boat that can come to your rescue more quickly than the Coast Guard.

If you have a cell signal, it is a good idea to have your cell phone handy while you contact the Coast Guard on channel 16. After establishing contact over the VHF, the Coast Guard may direct you to call a specific number from your cell phone if you have coverage.

FUN FACT: Sailors crossing oceans rely on VHF and a more powerful radio called Single Sideband (SSB). VHF is good for line-of-sight communication, but for long-distance, they use SSB radio signals that bounce off the ionosphere back to earth, enabling transmission over thousands of miles. Sailors crossing vast distances use SSB to listen to the powerful transmissions of the British Broadcasting Company

(BBC) News to keep up with what is going on in the world. BBC antennas have such a powerful reach, British nuclear submarines tune in after being submerged for months to determine whether the government is still functioning by checking whether BBC Radio is broadcasting.

CHAPTER 8

Advanced Radio Features

Once you learn about new radio capabilities, I'm sure you will agree it is confounding that boaters will spend thousands of dollars to reupholster their cockpit cushions but not spend a few hundred dollars to buy a state-ofthe-art VHF radio with Digital Selective Calling (DSC) and Automatic Identification System. These features are true lifesavers in emergencies. Equally mysterious is why many boaters who have DSC-capable radios don't bother to connect them to their GPS or register their information with the Coast Guard. In this section you will learn about:

- Digital Selective Calling (DSC) and Automated Emergency calls
- Advanced Features of DSC
- Automatic Identification System (AIS)
- Dual Watch
- Scan

- Cancelling Automated Emergency Calls

Here's a true story to underscore the importance of DSC and why it should be connected to your GPS.

Sailing friends had just splashed their 29-foot sailboat in the ocean after a winter of storage on land. Both a shakedown cruise for the boat and a way to smooth rusty sailing skills, the couple released the dock lines late in the afternoon with plans to drop anchor in a sheltered bay for the night. Winds were ideal at 15 to 20 miles an hour, and all seemed right with the sails, rigging, and boat.

Making notes about things that needed TLC, they noticed the microphone cord on the VHF radio had been nibbled to the wire by mice. They turned it on, but mice had eaten through it. One more repair for their list.

As they tacked toward their favorite anchorage, something struck the stern of their boat with force.

"What the...."

Rushing to the back of the boat, all they could see was an enormous disturbance in the water and their rudder floating away. What happened? A whale? A submerged log?

Windward of a rocky island, they dropped sails. The husband tied a line around his waist, jumped into chilly late spring water temperatures, and swam to the rudder. His wife reeled her husband and the rudder back on the winch, but they could not reattach the broken fittings. The rudder and boat were in danger of being carried downwind to crash on the rocky island shore with no way to steer.

Their first thought was to use the cell phone to call a friend and ask them to call the Coast Guard for help. Then, the skipper remembered the VHF radio had automated digital calling capability. Luckily, he had registered it with the Coast Guard and had connected it to their GPS. Even though he could not transmit Mayday on the microphone, his radio could do it for him. He flipped the red distress switch and heard the Coast Guard calling his boat by name. There was no way to answer, but then he listened to the Coast Guard give their grid coordinates and request that any boat in their vicinity render assistance until the Coast Guard arrived.

They were being carried downwind fast, and the sound of the waves crashing on the rocks got louder. They held each other and prepared to abandon their boat before impact but wanted to wait until the last possible moment, hoping the Coast Guard could get to them in time. Just then, a sportfishing boat sped up out of nowhere, threw them a line. They tied it to the front cleats, and the sportfishing boat towed them to safety.

If their VHF radio had not been registered with the Coast Guard or not connected to their GPS, they would have lost their boat and risked their lives getting to safety. A Coast Guard newsletter notes that 9 out of 10 alerts do not include GPS information because boaters have not correctly connected the VHF radio to their GPS units. What's more, 6 out of 10 alerts do not include the DSC and AIS information because boaters have not registered. When you finish this section, you will understand the importance of connecting these advanced radio features on your VHF radio to take the *search* out of Search and Rescue.

Digital Selective Calling (DSC) and Automated Emergency Calls

Search-and-rescue authorities learned long ago that, despite Coast Guard announcements to keep channel 16 clear for emergencies, recreational vessels tend to clutter the frequency with non-essential chatter, resulting in missed Mayday calls. Digital Selective Calling (DSC) technology helps overcome this problem and is now a standard on marine radios.

The principal purpose of DSC is **distress alerting**. Users can send a pre-configured distress message to emergency personnel and other DSC-equipped boats over channel 70 (which does not transmit voice) by pressing a red button. The message contains pertinent information about the boat, its Maritime Mobile Service Identity (MMSI) number, owner details, and emergency contact information. Your DSC-enabled radio is on the job whenever it is on, automatically monitoring channel 70 in the background, in addition to whatever voice channel you're on.

This means that the Coast Guard and other boaters in your immediate area receive a message that will include your vessel information, location, and perhaps even the nature of your emergency (if your radio is so equipped and proper information is input), allowing help to get to you quickly.

As a DSC generated distress call is digital, it can successfully travel and be understood farther than a standard voice distress call can. This means a greater chance of being heard and a greater chance to receive the help you desperately need.

To be able to make a VHF DSC DISTRESS call, you MUST have:

- **A DSC-capable VHF radio**. Your radio's operator manual will let you know if your radio has the proper capabilities.
- **An MMSI number**. Maritime Mobile Service Identity (MMSI) is a unique nine-digit number assigned to your vessel. These must be carefully programmed into your radio. Many radios must be shipped back to the factory if a mistake is made entering your MMSI. There is more on where and

how to obtain an MMSI number later in this section.

- **GPS connected to your radio or embedded in it**. Many newer generation radios come with embedded GPS. To properly put out a DSC DISTRESS call, your radio must have a GPS that is either embedded in the radio or external and wired in.

Following your radio's specific step-by-step instructions to activate a DISTRESS signal will digitally transmit a message of emergency that automatically identifies your vessel's information (name, make, etc.) as well as a GPS location. Again, for this to function properly your VHF radio MUST HAVE AN INTERNAL GPS OR BE SYNCED WITH AN EXTERNAL GPS SYSTEM.

NOTE: Distress calls activated without GPS encoding will not alert authorities to your location.

Repeated from Boat to Boat

Any DSC-enabled radio that picks up this data signal will sound a loud two-tone alarm and automatically switch over to channel 16 for voice communications between the vessel in distress and any DSC-equipped boat within transmission range that received the call.

A DSC transmission includes the priority of the call (distress, urgency, safety, routine), the intended recipient (all ships or a specific ship or station), and the transmitting boat's identity, location, and nature of distress. Above all, if your VHF radio has built in GPS or is connected by wire to your boat GPS, your distress call will include your exact position. This allows boats nearby to render assistance until the Coast Guard arrives.

The transmission takes about one-third of a second and is automatically repeated from the VHF of one boat to the VHF of another boat until a rescue authority answers. The radio does the work while the captain of the distressed vessel attempts to deal with the emergency. Because the signal is digital, it has a better chance than a voice call of getting through in rough conditions. It is like having an extra crew member that keeps cool amid the confusion and chaos of a potentially life and death situation.

Other Advantages of DSC

The earth's curvature limits the range of normal VHF radio operations to about 20 miles depending upon antenna height. When you press the DSC distress button, other boats retransmit any emergency signals received. When passed automatically on channel 70 from one boat to the next, the effective range of a distress call can be many times greater than your own boat's VHF range. DSCequipped radios help save lives by retransmitting the distress signal and extending the range of the distressed vessel.

Remember, you **must** set up your DSC-enabled radio to interface with a GPS receiver to broadcast position information. If you've ever heard the Coast Guard or a fellow boater struggling to get accurate information from a mariner in distress, you understand the value of this feature. DSC technology is a significant advancement in communications and is reason enough to buy a new radio if yours is not DSC-equipped.

DSC automatic emergency calling over VHF radio is always the fastest way for a boater to summon assistance from the closest rescuers. Broadcasting your exact location takes the *search* out of Search and Rescue.

I cannot overstate the importance of DSC. While you are dealing with an emergency on your boat, your VHF radio works non-stop to bring help.

Obtaining an MMSI Number

You can obtain an MMSI number through BoatUS or the US Power Squadron.

If you are considering traveling internationally as an American, you need to file Form 605 online with the

American Federal Communications Commission to obtain a Ship Station License—which comes with an MMSI.

Obtain an MMSI online for domestic US waters through BoatUS or the US Power Squadron*

To obtain an MMSI for international travel, download FCC Form 605 and apply for a ship station license.

Visit these websites for more information about obtaining an MMSI.

BOATUS:
https://www.boatus.com/products-and-services/membership/mmsi

US Power Squadron:
https://www.usps.org/php/ mmsi_new/.

CAUTION: Some VHF radios allow an MMSI number to be programmed in ONE TIME—and require shipping the unit back to the factory for changes. If you have ANY aspirations to travel abroad, apply for the Ship Station License.

NOTE: No matter where you are from or where you travel in your boat, you need to obtain an MMSI number for your radio's DSC operations to be functional.

Canceling a False Distress Alert

In the unlikely event you set off your radio's automated emergency function unintentionally, or you recover from an emergency and no longer need assistance, **you must cancel your distress call** as quickly as possible.

Cancel a call by first powering the unit OFF. Powering off stops the distress message from being broadcast. After it is fully off, turn the unit back ON and switch to channel 16 on **high power,** transmit:

"All stations. All stations. All stations.

Cancel my distress call of [time of call].

This is [vessel name] *at* [position].

[Vessel name]. "

The Coast Guard is serious about putting the lives of mariners and first responders in danger, and any hoax callers face up to 10 years in prison, $250,000 in fines, plus the cost of the search.

There is no MMSI entered DSC is disabled and your distress calling will not work.

This Icom radio has not had an MMSI programmed in and is therefore not capable of making DSC calls, including automated distress calls.

Individual (Non-Emergency) Direct Calls

Boaters have been slow to utilize non-emergency capabilities of DSC radios, but I encourage you to practice using these features. With DSC, your radio can direct-dial another VHF (via its MMSl number) and relay your boat's grid coordinates. Your VHF can also *ping* another radio.

Are you wondering what that means?

Well, imagine your wife and kids have gone off exploring in the dinghy. If you dial the DSC-equipped handheld VHF they took along, it will display the dinghy's position on your chart plotter. This feature is known as **position polling**. When cruising with friends, it's a handy way to keep track of everyone.

For people who fish, it's a discreet way to let your good friends know where the fish are biting. It is also a good meetup tool. If you have boat problems and call a tow service, they can send you a poll request and drop your position as a waypoint on their plotter.

DSC also allows ship-to-ship direct digital calling. Your DSC-capable radio and MMSI number enable you to directly *call* another boat with an MMSI number you have programmed into your radio. You can pre-select a working channel, and when the receiving vessel answers your call, you are both on the working channel without ever having connected on channel 16. The call will not go out on channel 70, which is reserved for digital emergency signaling.

DSC for Discretion

Here's a good reason to learn all the advanced features of your VHF radio.

Glen and I had just landed a sizeable dorado—mahi mahi on menus—and were ready to return to harbor. The fish were still biting however, and we wanted to let our friends know about the hot spot—a floating pallet a few miles offshore. With the Maritime Mobile Service Identity (MMSI) of our friend's boat already entered in the address list of our VHF radio we initiated a "position send" call via Digital Selective Calling (DSC), allowing us to privately send our coordinates. Our friends found the floating pallet and hauled in their own catch. If we had made a voice call, there would have been a stampede. Instead, we discretely sent our coordinates directly to a specific boat using their MMSI.

In order to use these advanced features of your DSC radio, you need to connect the radio to both the GPS receiver and the chart plotter. The GPS receiver sends the position data to the radio, and the radio will transmit this data when requested to other stations. The radio must also be connected to the chart plotter, so that when the radio receives position information it will output the data to the chart plotter for display.

Take the time to read your VHF manual and practice these calling features with your buddy boat. If it's time to upgrade your electronics, make sure they are capable of advanced DSC functions.

Automatic Identification System

AIS is a collection of transponders (transmitting devices) that send out a ship's detailed information including vessel position, course, and speed. Most newer VHF radios come equipped with a built in AIS receiver—however, not all have a transponder. In other words, unless your VHF DSC-equipped radio has a transponder, your radio can *pick up* the detailed AIS information of other vessels but will not *transmit* one for your vessel.

If you plan to buy a DSC-equipped VHF radio, spend a bit more and make sure it is transponder and GPS equipped. With an AIS-equipped, receiving-only VHF radio, you will be able to identify ships in your vicini ty that have AIS transponders, but your radio must have transponder capability to be seen by other ships. In high waves or storm conditions your boat does not show up very well on radar, while your digitally transmitted AIS signal will show not only your position but the name, length and type of your vessel.

AIS enhances visual and radar identification, and it can be a true lifesaver on the waters. You can display information on your VHF base unit display or connect it to your chart plotter. Typically, the report includes the other boat's distance from your vessel, bearing from your vessel, speed, the direction of travel, and time and distance of its Closest Point of Approach (CPA).

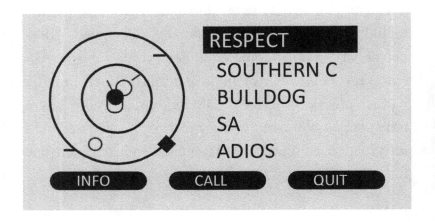

The image on the previous page represents a Standard Horizon GX2200 model base unit radio displaying lists four AIS-transmitting vessels within my range by name.

If I select the vessel Adios from this list, I can see all of the boat's details provided by its AIS transponder, including:

- The vessel's full name.
- Its bearing from my ship (not its course heading).
- The vessel's CPA—how close it will come to my boat based on current conditions.
- The vessel's Time to Closest Point of Approach (TCPA)—how long it will be until we are at our CPA.
- Its Speed Over Ground (SOG)—how fast it is moving from GPS tracking.

You can see all this information in the following image:

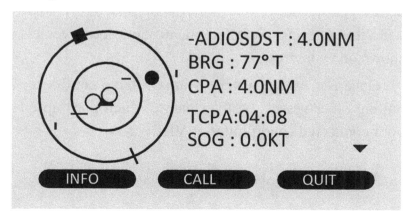

Another nice feature of some AIS-receiving VHF radios is alarms you can configure to a specific task. Depending on the model, you can set an alarm to alert you when an AIS-transmitting vessel comes within a certain distance of your boat or if a vessel's CPA falls within a specific time limit.

This system also helps in reduced-visibility situations, such as heavy fog, by identifying close-by vessels with specific names and courses of travel. This identification enables you to initiate detailed radio contact to help minimize confusion and risk of collision. It is a huge benefit to be able to call others by name. Remember, not every boat on the water will appear on your AIS—just those equipped with a transmitting AIS.

It can be awkward to read and comprehend AIS information in a rushed, adrenaline-pumping situation. If you have an AIS-capable VHF radio, take some time before getting out on the water to familiarize yourself with the settings. Practice identifying local vessels shown on your screen.

Once out on the waters, you will have confidence hailing other vessels by their name, which pops up on your connected chart plotter or VHF screen.

Dual Watch

Dual watch is a radio feature that enables you to monitor channel 16 while you are on a different channel. Your radio does this by checking channel 16 for traffic approximately every two seconds in the background. This constant monitoring allows you to comply with your obligation to monitor channel 16 for emergency traffic while also monitoring a working channel you use to reach out to buddy boats.

While this can be a helpful tool, it is essential to understand potential drawbacks. Channel 16 is the default channel for your VHF radio. If you are attempting to carry on a conversation on a working channel (such as 68) while in dual watch, your radio will switch you back to 16 for that channel's traffic and you will have no idea what was said by your communication partner on 68.

Dual watch is a powerful and effective tool, but it may be a good idea to use it for dual monitoring rather than conversing.

Scan

The scan feature enables your radio to check a particular set or range of channels rapidly and stop where it finds traffic. The scan feature could be helpful if you are new to an area and looking for a local hailing channel, a cruiser radio net, or to determine which channels aren't in use so you can choose a working channel.

Scan features vary widely from manufacturer to manufacturer, so be sure to read your radio's user's manual to learn your radio's specific capabilities. Some let you choose the channels or range of channels to scan, and some do not even have the scan capability. If the owner's manual of your VHF is no longer part of your onboard reference, you can download one from the internet for free from your manufacturer's website.

The Three Biggest Mistakes Boaters Make with VHF DSC Radio

- **Mistake #1**: There's probably not a person reading this who uses a 15-year-old phone, television, or computer. But for some reason, there are boaters out there relying on an old VHF radio that is not equipped with DSC to signal that you are in distress. Today's DSC-VHF radios have a distress button that can send a Mayday and relay your position to rescue authorities. The radio keeps sending the signal until the Coast Guard responds.

- **Mistake #2**: Not bothering to get an MMSI number and then register a DSC-VHF with the Coast Guard. The MMSI number is a unique registration number assigned to your vessel and used with the vessel's DSC-VHF radio. Organizations such as Boat US issue MMSI numbers to their members at no cost. Once obtained, you **must** enter the MMSI number into your VHF radio to benefit from all its potential and lifesaving technology. Registering your radio provides potential rescuers important information about you, your boat, and whom to contact in an emergency.

- **Mistake #3**: Not reading the owner's manual that came with your VHF and familiarizing yourself with your radio's features. Your DSC-VHF radio manual contains essential information about the features of your radio and how to install it. If you do not correctly install the radio or connect it to your boat's GPS or chart plotter, you are putting yourself and your crew in danger. DSC is the fastest way to receive help in an emergency.

*****

What DSC VHF Radios Do

Let's review:

- Provide one-touch emergency capability that sends out a vessel's unique registered MMSI number and, if properly connected to a GPS, gives the vessel's position in latitude and longitude coordinates.

- Allows an inexperienced crew member unfamiliar with radio equipment to send a continuous distress message by pressing a single button.

- Continue sending a distress signal even if everyone on the boat is incapacitated or otherwise engaged.

- Use a known MMSI to contact another DSCequipped vessel directly. Like a telephone, it will alert your radio that you have a call and then automatically switch you to the channel your caller has selected. This automation means you do not have to monitor high-traffic channels or hail yachting friends on hailing and distress frequencies.

- Use a polling feature to transmit your vessel's position to a DSC-equipped station if both vessels are GPS-connected.

- Initiate a search-and-rescue operation when you push the distress button.

What DSC VHF Radios Do Not Do

Perform any of these functions without registering for a unique MMSI number, inputting the code, and connecting with GPS.

*****

Interesting Fact About AIS

Sometimes it takes something terrible to happen to point the way to new technology. AIS is just such a case.

After the oil tanker Exxon Valdez ran aground in Alaska's Prince William Sound, spilling eleven million gallons of crude oil into a sensitive natural environment, the U.S. government realized it needed a way to track dangerous cargo as well as monitor suspicious vessels in U.S. waters. It took years, but eventually, a company developed AIS, and the world has readily embraced it.

Initially, AIS improved *situational awareness* for vessels and provided tracking capabilities similar to air traffic control. Before AIS, navigators, and captains depended on visual navigation, radar, and voice communications to avoid collisions.

Today, AIS is available to recreational boaters. It automatically communicates and transmits a vessel's location to other ships and shore-based Coast Guard without the risk of miscommunication and human error.

While traveling the Great Loop of America, we used it almost every day—coordinating passing situations, looking for buddy boats, identifying tugs and barges around the bend of rivers, and more. You will be glad you took the time and effort to install and learn this important system.

CHAPTER 9

Cruiser Nets

Now that you are rockin' n rollin' on the VHF radio, you'll enjoy yourself even more by participating in Cruiser Nets. You can even run one! It's really fun—but don't take my word for it, try it yourself. Here's why you should participate and how to be the head honcho.

Cruiser nets form in popular places *such as* Boot Key Harbor, *Marathon, Florida*

The morning VHF radio network is essential for a boat cruiser's day-to-day life. Called *cruiser nets*, these controlled, moderated radio gatherings of boats at a particular anchorage or cruising ground, occur daily at a scheduled time on a specific radio channel. Most moderators announce the net on channel 16 just before the start of the broadcast.

Combination coffee klatch and radio show, a well-run cruiser net includes helpful information for all the boats and creates a sense of community by connecting and welcoming boaters.

Cruiser nets are run by whoever is willing to volunteer. Where there is a long-term liveaboard community, the role typically rotates through a regular group. In more transient places, it helps if everyone takes a turn now and again. The problem is knowing what to say. Here is a script in case you get recruited. In this example I use my base on the Sea of Cortez, San Carlos, Mexico.

Net Controller Transcript

1. **Welcome**. Good morning and welcome to the San Carlos Cruisers' Net. Does anyone have emergency, medical, or priority traffic?

2. **Introduction**. This is [your name] aboard [your vessel] with [names of others on board]. Today is [day of week, date].

3. **Net specifics**. This is a controlled net. This net meets 365 days a year at 9 AM local time. When you check-in, please give your boat name only and wait to be recognized by net control.

4. **New arrivals**. Do we have any new arrivals? Please tell us about yourself, tell us who's onboard, where you are from, and a bit of your plans.

5. **Departures**. Do we have departures? Anyone leaving the area today or already underway?

6. **Check-ins**. Alright, let's go ahead with check-ins. Come with your boat name, and I will repeat it to let you know I've heard you. Any other check-ins within the sound of my voice, come now. [Provide a rough count of the total number of check-ins].

7. **Weather**. Does anyone have the tides and weather this morning?

8. **Overseas Mail Call**. Is there anyone who can carry flat-stamped mail to Canada or the U.S.? Are there any vessels holding mail for another vessel?

9. **Crew positions**. Does anyone need crew, or does anyone want to find a crew position?

10. **Lost and found**. Did anyone lose or find anything?

11. General Announcements. Let's move to the General announcements.

12. **Local assistance**. Labor or services wanted or offered.

13. **Treasures of the bilge**. Does anyone have anything to buy, sell, swap, trade or give away?

14. **Last call**. Is there anything else for the net?

15. **Salutation**. That's the end of the cruisers net for today. Boats in the harbor please remember to switch back to low power. Thanks, everyone. This is [boat name] clear.

It's a great idea to check in with the local cruiser net when you first arrive at an anchorage. If you are cruising with children aboard, it's a great way to find other boats with kids. Nets are also an effective tool to meet neighbors and get tips for the area, such as the name of a good dentist, best fuel prices, veterinary care, buddy boating, help with repairs and parts, local sights, attractions, and so much more.

You can find information on the schedule of local cruiser nets in the most updated cruising guides or on Active Captain, a crowd-sharing program on electronic charts. Keep pen and paper ready to jot down boat or business names throughout the broadcast. Also, think about how you wish to introduce your boat as far as vessel name, your name(s), your hailing port, kids on board, and the like. You do not have to share any information that makes you feel uncomfortable.

Let's examine a few aspects of cruiser nets that sometimes confuse first-timers.

Net Controllers

One of the most common concerns for first-time net participants is the function of the net controller. VHF radio is push-to-talk. Without a net controller, the cruiser net would be chaos, and participants could overlap each other's announcements. Just like calling another boat from your own, working with a net controller is easy once you understand the ground rules.

The moderator's primary function is to control the net. You may hear them say, "This is a controlled net. Give your boat name and wait to be recognized before passing your traffic." In other words, when you want to talk, say your vessel name, and wait until the net controller calls on you. Sometimes several boats will state their names at once—when this happens, the net controller either chooses one they heard clearly or asks everyone to try again.

If someone needs to buy something, say a spark plug wrench to service their Yamaha dinghy outboard, they listen for the segment of the net when the announcer says, "Treasures of the Bilge" or "Buy, Sell, Trade,

Giveaway." and then calls in with their boat name. The moderator will then ask, "Anybody out there?" That is the signal for boaters to join in. They reply with their boat name one time and wait to be recognized. When the moderator responds with the person's boat name, they can tell the controller what they need.

Remember to give your boat name only and wait to be called on every time you have something to say, **even if you are just replying to a general question that someone has asked**.

An example of general announcements might be letting other cruisers know about a pickleball game, or someone might call in to ask if anyone knows where the holding tank pump-out is available in the harbor or ask for recommendations for a doctor in the area. These are perfect examples of the sort of community-driven help that makes a net valuable.

Some Net Basics

Four things that will make participating in the nets (and the flurry of radio calls afterward) a little easier.

Describe Your Boat and Location

If you are looking for help on a project or offering something to give away or sell, be prepared to provide a clear description of your vessel and its location in the anchorage. Remember that from 100 yards away, many boats look the same, even to a seasoned eye. Do you have an enclosure on the flybridge or bimini? Are you on a numbered mooring ball? Say so! Anything to make you easily identifiable from a distance. Boat names are impossible to read from far away, especially if driving a dinghy.

Weather

Most nets have a short weather section and often give high and low tides and a local, general forecast for the anchorage. This information may be from a source the moderator likes but never make your decisions based on secondhand weather. Use other sources to compare and verify what the net shares. The author has seen an entire fleet of sailboats in the Pacific clobbered by a weather bomb when one strongly opinionated skipper swayed the opinion of other captains about a questionable forecast.

Radio Power

Use high power to make calls on the net. You want to make sure everyone participating can hear you. If you switch to a working channel to talk to someone, you can consider low power.

Up and Down

Speaking of switching to a working channel, here is a good rule of thumb: 72 and up! 68 and down!"

Huh?

"And up" and "and down" are channel directives used in busy anchorages. There is so much radio traffic in some harbors that it becomes a challenge to find a clear working channel ahead of time. As a result, it has become common practice to pick a starting point (say, channel 72) and a direction (up or down).

Suppose one day, during the cruisers net I ask for help troubleshooting my Yamaha dinghy outboard. I get a response from the captain of *Barefoot Gal*, who says she can help me. I want to coordinate a meeting time and give her directions to my boat. After establishing contact, I may say, "*Barefoot Gal*, let's go seven-two and up." *Barefoot Gal* would then reply, "Copy that, *Star Dust*. Seven-two and up."

I would then head to channel 72 first and, if it is busy, I go up one channel. If that is busy, I continue up until I find a clear channel among those authorized as working channels. With luck, *Barefoot Gal* hears the same traffic and ends up on the same channel.

While this may not be a perfect system, it works. It also offers an element of adventure to the simple act of making contact. If I bounce around up from 72 and never find *Barefoot Gal*, I will head back to our original contact channel and hail them again, just as we learned in the hailing section of this book.

The nets only work when people participate, so tune in and join in! Be sure to enunciate, speak slowly, and position yourself to keep your mic out of the wind. You will soon enjoy the rewards of friendship and camaraderie that come with participating in the net.

CHAPTER 10

Self-Reliance

Okay. Last words on the subject of VHF radio. I've had great adventures, visited lots of truly incredible places, and met some amazing people through years of sailing and boating. So many, that I kept wanting to add more to this book, to give you as many stories as possible from decades of experience. My desire was to present you with lessons learned in case you ever face a similar situation. As you've seen in this guide, when you take off on a boat you must be self-reliant and know what to do in an emergency.

There is something deeply transformational about being self-sufficient on a womb-like boat. And few things are as enjoyable as spending time with the community of adventurers you encounter along the way. But like any boater who has been around for a while, I've also had rough times and self-doubt on the water. There have been situations where I was not sure what to do or if I would make it.

Boating is more than sundowners and beach potlucks. Things can get dodgy fast, and it is vital you consider the VHF radio as one of the most essential lifesaving tools on your boat.

You must know so many things to be proficient on the water that it can be overwhelming to meet all the demands. Hopefully you gained some experience here in dealing with emergencies that you will never be forced to use. If you have gotten this far in the book, you are the type of person who approaches things with your best effort, and that's all anyone can expect of you.

Whatever you do and encounter, don't stop learning and stretching yourself. Your nautical skills will come together, and the best feeling in the world is knowing you are good at what you do. Keep grabbing opportunities to get out on the water and communicate over your VHF. Soon you will be capable and confident.

Finally, on a personal note, I hope you are as excited the thousandth time you go out on the water as the first time. I was. I am.

NOTE: You can read about the authors' circumnavigation adventures in her two international bestselling books; Escape from the Ordinary and Crossing Pirate Waters. A book on the Great Loop is

forthcoming and you can read articles at:
https://www.juliebradleyauthor.com/

*****

Did you enjoy *Mayday, Mayday! Mariners' Guide to VHF Radio*?

If so, I'd very much appreciate a review. Your review—even a few words—helps others find the book (and keeps me wanting to write the next one). Thank you for your support.

—Julie Bradley

TEMPLATES AND EXTRAS

Channel Usage

Channel	Use
16	International hailing and distress. All vessels required to monitor. Hail on 16, then immediately switch to working channel.
09	Hailing channel. In some states, bridge or lock channel. In some states, bridge or lock channel. Can use for radio checks.
13	Ship-to-ship hailing and working channel. In some states, bridge or lock channel. Automatically low power.
22A	Reserved for coast guard.
01, 07-11, 18,19, 63, 67, 79, 80	Commercial use only.
70	Digital channel and cannot be used for voice calls.
68, 69, 71, 72, 78A	General communications between all types of vessels. Good choices for working channels.

	Handheld		Base	
	Low (1 Watt)	High (5 – 6 Watts)	Low (1 Watt)	High (25 Watts)
Typical Range	200 Yards	3 Miles	1 Mile	12Miles*
Emergency calls & relays for emergency calls		✓		✓
Bridge or lock		✓	✓	
Passing situation	✓	If no response on low	✓	
Nearby boat or business	✓		✓	
Office/ fuel dock of marina you are in	✓		✓	
Marina you are approaching		✓	✓	
Marina at distance		Unlikely to reach		✓
Cruiser's net		✓		✓

If someone has a problem hearing you, go to next greater range combination. For example, jump from handheld high power to using the base unit on higher power.

*With antenna at least 18' above waterline; higher antennas will get greater range, often up to 20 or more miles.

A	Alfa	N	November
B	Bravo	O	Oscar
C	Charlie	P	Papa
D	Delta	Q	Quebec
E	Echo	R	Romeo
F	Foxtrot	S	Sierra
G	Golf	T	Tango
H	Hotel	U	Uniform
I	India	V	Victor
J	Juliet	W	Whiskey
K	Kilo	X	X-ray
L	Lima	Y	Yankee
M	Mike	Z	Zulu

Radio Quick Check

If you don't hear a reply to your call, check:

- Channel
- Volume
- Squelch
- High/Low Power

If all are correct and you expected an answer, consider a radio check.

USE CHANNEL 16 • HIGH POWER

Mayday: For life-threatening emergencies only.

Fire, sinking, MOB, life-threatening problems.

PAN-PAN (pawn-pawn): Emergencies that do not have an immediate risk to life.

Firmly press the mic and say:

"Mayday, Mayday, Mayday" (or PAN-PAN)

"This is [name of boat]. We are located at [GPS location]."

Briefly state:

- nature of emergency and help needed
- number of people on board an any injuries

"Mayday, Mayday, Mayday" (or PAN-PAN)"

Release mic and wait 30 seconds for reply. If no reply, repeat. If at all possible, stay by radio to answer return calls.

If You Hear an Emergency Call

1. Respond if no one else has or if you can communicate better.

2. Write down location of emergency.

3. Offer assistance or reply to the Coast Guard or others.

4. Continue to monitor the situation until resolved.

Automated Emergency Calls

Raise the hinged **red distress shield** and press the emergency button underneath for three to five seconds until the screen shows that the emergency call feature has been activated.

A digital Mayday call will be made automatically, showing your boat name and location. If possible, stay near the radio on channel 16 to answer. This is powerful tool for getting help but you **MUST**:

- Program your MMSI number into the radio.

AND

- Have an internal GPS on your radio or you must have connected your radio's GPS to the VHF.

Squelch

Use squelch to adjust the amount of static you hear. Turning squelch UP reduces static but may also filter out weaker radio traffic. Turning it DOWN will help you hear fainter traffic but you'll also hear more static.

Weather Radio

WEATHER FORECASTS

On U.S. radios, press the WX button to access to access the weather channels. Listen for the loudest and clearest of the eight weather channels. General weather will be given as well as detailed weather for zones in the area. To find your zone:

- Check NOAA Coastal Weather page at *https://www.weather.gov/marine/usamz*
- Click on progressively smaller area to find your zone.
- Switch back to a VHF channel (usually 16) when done.

WEATHER ALERTS

If there is dangerous weather in your area, your radio may sound an alarm. Usually, when you silence the alarm, the radio will automatically go to the weather channel so that you can listen to the alert. Be sure to switch back to channel 16 afterward.

CPSIA information can be obtained
at www.ICGtesting.com
Printed in the USA
LVHW021137260422
717217LV00015B/702